# w York Cave

ance
t

Steep
rop

Dock

Fox
Room

Overlaugh

Broken Room

Brook(?)

Spring
Room

Ampitheatre

0 100
Feet

N

by Richard F. Logan
ap by Prof. John H. Cook
Annual Report of N.Y. State Museum
itions from personal reconnaissance by Clay Perry

# UNDERGROUND EMPIRE

# UNDERGROUND EMPIRE

*WONDERS AND TALES OF NEW YORK CAVES*

BY CLAY PERRY

IRA J. FRIEDMAN, INC.
Port Washington, Long Island, N. Y.

UNDERGROUND EMPIRE


Reissued in 1966 by Ira J. Friedman, Inc. by arrangement with
Frederick Ungar Publishing Company

Library of Congress Catalog Card No: 66-21380

Manufactured in the United States of America

EMPIRE STATE HISTORICAL PUBLICATIONS SERIES XLI

To

PAUL A. PERRY

A Good Spelunker

# FOREWORD

Since the days when they were man's first shelter, caves have fascinated the human mind. Interest in what lies hidden is inherent. The folk imagination clothes with wonder the invisible. It peoples the dark and inaccessible cavern with strange beings and it provides them with fabulous surroundings. Careful science finds beneath earth's surface different but no less wondrous things.

The caves of New York State have told her geologists and her anthropologists much about the times before history was recorded. Since then writers, known and unknown, have enlivened their narrative accounts of life within the region by tales of the uses our forefathers made of hollows under the surfaces of our land. And our folklore is aglitter with stories of magic subterranean halls in which beautiful horses stand hitched to shiny surreys, golden books lie on golden tables, strange skaters skim the surfaces of ponds frozen over in midsummer, the ghosts of slain Indians beat death-songs upon their water-drums.

Clay Perry has done all lovers of Americana a welcome service with his reports on his researches in earth-hidden places. His descriptions of the underground recesses of New England have given us an exciting foretaste of what we may expect from him. We know that he is indefatigable in research, intrepid in exploration, unfailingly observant, ever aware of scientific values and the rewards that derive from a lively imaginative approach and a sense of humor.

Now that Mr. Perry has told us of the caves of New York in his pleasant prose, we urge that he continue his labors. New England and the Empire State lie behind. Ahead, under the vast surface of America, lie countless caves that deserve his personal attention. We would like to have him tell us about them.

CARL CARMER

# ACKNOWLEDGEMENTS

During the study of the Empire State's caves and some of its mines and quarries, for the purpose of compiling this book in "The American Caves Series," I have been generously assisted by a considerable number of persons and institutions, and almost all of them have given me this aid eagerly, fascinated by the subject.

I am particularly indebted to A. T. Shorey, of the Forests and Lands Division, New York State Department of Conservation, who was the first person whom I asked for data on caves and who served as my chief guide in research and field work over a long period, and to Darwin Benedict of the Department of Commerce, Public Relations Division, who acted as second mate to Mr. Shorey; to Alvin G. Whitney, Assistant Director, New York State Museum, who made available to me the facilities of the Museum and its library; to Professor John H. Cook, Geologist at the Museum, whose field reports on caves and careful scrutiny of much of the manuscript proved invaluable.

Also to William Endicott, Chairman, Albany Chapter, Adirondack Mountain Club, and members of this club; Vincent J. Schaefer, of the General Electric Company's research laboratories at Schenectady, and members of the Mohawk Valley Hiking Club; Dr. George H. Chadwick of Catskill, geologist and historian, and members of the Natural Science Association of the Catskills; Professor Louis C. Jones, Director, New York State Historical Society, and Editor, *New York Folklore;* Acting State Geologist, John G. Broughton.

Dr. Frederick Pough, Director, Mineralogy Department, American Museum of Natural History, New York City; Miss Fanny Clark, Librarian, Harlan H. Ballard Historical Library, Berkshire Atheneum, Pittsfield, Mass.; Roger Johnson, Springfield and Hockanum, Mass., who first inspired the project of books about caves and loaned his entire collection of scrapbooks, index files and photographs, and joined in the field work; Frank Solari, New York City, cave photographer and speleologist; Carl S. Hulett, Jr., Editor, *The Chatham (N. J.) Courier;* Dr. Harold W. Thompson, President, New York Folklore Society; Carl Carmer, New York City, Honorary Vice President of the same society and collector of much folklore and legend; Robert Deardorff, New York City; J. M. Mathes Advertising Agency; the International Salt Company; Dr. E. Eugene Barker, Albany; Miss Lydia Neubuck, Adirondack Natural Bridge and Caverns, Pottersville, N. Y.; Stephen H. E. Pell and Milo S. King, Fort Ticonderoga; Erwin Sloane and Arch Merrill, Rochester; Charles E. Mohr, Director, Education Department, Academy of Natural Sciences, Philadelphia; Virgil Clymer, Alfred G. Platt, and H. W. Hall, Howe Caverns; D. C. Robinson, Knox Cave; Frank W. Pugsley, Pittsford, N. Y.; Dr. Edward S. C. Smith, Union College, Schenectady; William J. Stephenson, President, National Speleological Society, Washington, D. C.; Richard F. Logan, and many other members of this society; Mr. and Mrs. Gerald Carson and daughters, Millerton, N. Y.; Warren Walker, Albany; Arthur Van Voris, Cobleskill, N. Y., and others whose names appear here and there in the text of this book.

May I also express my sincere thanks to these persons and organizations for permission to reproduce the photographs and sketches named here: Loman Thomson for the cave nymphs; Champlain Valley Archeological Society for the Indian cave grave; Publicity Division, New York State Department of Commerce, for the Natural Stone Bridge, the cave at Glens Falls, the gorge of Ausable Chasm, Watkins Glen, and the Ostertag Committee; LeRoy Foote for the Amber Grotto; North River Studio, courtesy A. T. Shorey, for Chimney Mountain; Daniel Smiley, Jr., for Mohonk Caves; the management of Howe Caverns for Alcove of the Angels, cross section of a stalagmite, and a wedding at old Howes Cave; Anthony W. Thurston for the self-photo at Bonaparte's Cave; Charles E. Mohr for Niagara Falls Caverns and the pictures of bats; Frank Solari for the picture of the author being a human fly; International Salt Co. for the Retsof Salt Mine; New York Central Railroad for the giant pothole; and Darwin Benedict for the picture of Miss Bess Little.

# TABLE OF CONTENTS

# LIST OF ILLUSTRATIONS

# INTRODUCTION

Good cave country in the Empire State is concentrated mostly within a broad-based triangle in the northeastern part of the state. Its base is the Taconic Range of mountains which roughly parallels the geographical and political boundaries between New York, Vermont, Massachusetts, and Connecticut. This triangle has one tip resting upon Crown Point, in the north, the southern point in the vicinity of Poughkeepsie or Newburgh, the western tip at Watertown.

Within this area lies most of the limestone of the sort in which true caves and caverns are formed, likewise deposits of many minerals, save salt, which brought about the opening of some of the oldest mines in the United States, especially iron mines. This large area has been the subject of much study by geologists, paleontologists, archeologists, mineralogists, speleologists, and just plain spelunkers. This study is still going on, chiefly under the auspices of the state of New York through the University of the State of New York and its departments at Albany, but also by independent scientists at universities and colleges and other institutions, as well as those employed by industry.

As this is a book about New York State's underworld of darkness, both natural and man made, it is appropriate that this eastern area should be considered first, and because the most interesting caves are further confined to the Taconic Range itself, and the Schoharie County area, that it should begin at the base of the cave country triangle.

There are other caves scattered about the great Empire State, ranging even to the Pennsylvania border and, most picturesquely, to Niagara Falls on the northwest; and there is one of the most remarkable mines in the world near Syracuse, a busy, glittering scene of operations, far, far underground, with some one hundred and twenty miles of tunnels dug by men and machines, lighted by electricity, traversed by electric trains. (See Chapter 18, *"Salt of the Earth."*)

All this is the underground empire of the Empire State. Let us make an entrance to this unique underworld with some of the geologists who have studied it from very early times.

N. S. Shaler was one of the early students of speleology and in 1887 wrote an article in *Scribner's Magazine*, Vol. 1-29, titled *"Caverns and Cavern Life."* In this twenty-four page article Shaler refers to New York caves as follows:

> So far as the present writer has been able to observe American Caverns, they have been limited to regions south of the vast field occupied by the ice-sheet of the latest glacial period.
>
> But in New York and elsewhere there are some small caverns which were within that field of ice. It is an important task for students to find whether these caverns existed before the ice period or whether they have been formed since that time.
>
> If they survived the glacial period, as seems likely, then they afford valuable evidence to show that the ice did not wear away as great a depth from the surface of the country as is commonly supposed.

Professor John H. Cook, of the New York State Museum staff, who made the first official survey of caves for that institution in 1905-06, does not go into this study, but others tell us that eastern New York State was completely covered with ice to a depth of 2,000 feet or more, but that evidently the glacial drift did not destroy its caverns as much as it did those to the east, in New England, which is why New York State caves on the whole are larger than those of New England.

There is a great variety of limestone in New York State, as well as of shales. The cave-bearing limestones lie mostly within that triangle indicated above.

In Cook's survey he found that in Albany and Schoharie Counties, for instance, are three cavern zones, designated as the

Onondaga, the Becraft, and the Manlius, and that the latter is ideal in composition for the forming of caves. Another kind, Coeyman's limestone, being more resistant to erosive forces, has usually caves that are deep, vertical shafts worn along joint planes and occasionally extending into the Manlius below.

Of unusual interest is the fact that in Becraft limestone "solution begins in its lowest beds, subsequent enlargement being principally due to the falling of slabs from the ceiling and their removal by water."

The caverns of New York State form a natural drainage system, its development dependent upon the geological structure of the region.

As the writer of this book is not a geologist, and more of a spelunker than a scientific speleologist, he has had to depend a great deal upon the work of trained scientists for descriptions of geological features, just as he has had to depend greatly upon the work and reports of many a speleologist, spelunker, or collector of folklore—for it is obviously a physical impossibility for any one person in less than a long lifetime to travel to all the caverns in the state, much less crawl in and through all of them.

But he has visited dozens of caves and, indeed, has seen with his own eyes most of those that are sizeable and have picturesque features, ranging from the northern Taconics to the Catskills, Albany and Schoharie regions, the Adirondacks, and to Buffalo and Niagara Falls.

There is buried history in this Underground Empire, and a great deal of folklore; and folklore, according to Joseph Chase Allen, writing in *Yankee Magazine,* is *"The faculty of remembering things that never happened."*

But they *might* have happened.

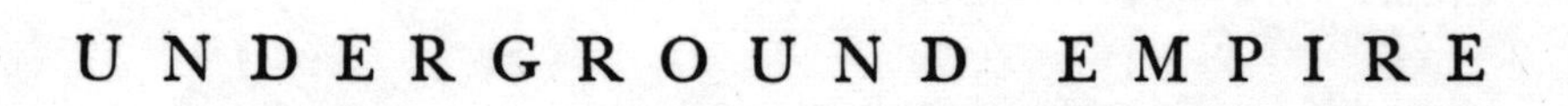

# UNDERGROUND EMPIRE

## *Chapter I*

# IN AN INDIAN OVEN

THEY were going to put prisoners in this hole in the rock, as had been done in the notorious Newgate Prison at Simsbury, Connecticut, the first Federal prison in this country. Fortunately for the poor wretches who might have been buried alive in a damp, silent tomb with nothing to do but carve themselves out places to lie down or stand up, the project never did go through. The authorities, after a visit to Indian Oven Cave, decided it was not an ideal place for even the criminals of Dutchess County to languish out their sentences.

Indian Oven Cave was discovered by a dog, to the poor canine's tragic disappointment, for the dog died in the bottom of the cave. Indian Oven Cave was named for a formation at some little distance from its entrance which may once have been used as a cooking place by the aborigines, but probably was not; it just was a rock that looked like an oven. The cave itself is in no way comparable to an oven of any sort, and it certainly is never hot. It is located on a ridge or bench of rock, one of three such ledges that run north and south along the side and summit of a wooded hill which parallels New York State Highway 22, and the Harlem Line of the New York Central Railroad, and it is directly west of the tiny Mount Rhiga station on this railroad, which is in the extreme northern end of the town of Millerton, Dutchess County.

The marked approach to it, however, begins in the town of Ancram, Columbia County, at the summer residence of Mr. and Mrs. Gerald Carson, New York City folks who, with their two young daughters, have welcomed many a spelunking party to hike through their grounds, up across a field which has grown from an open cow pasture to a thicket, from there to a bar-way at the edge of some rather dense woods, and thence along an old wood-road which peters to a trail. Keeping to the left fork where the road branches, the trail leads directly to the yawning sink-hole, at the bottom of which is the entrance to the cave.

It is not easy to find, as one party of spelunkers discovered in a half day's strenuous search of the hill on a hot summer day, finally giving up and calling for help from the writer, who had visited it twice. And then it was Sally and Gay Carson who led us unerringly to the cave and went in to see it for the first time in their young lives. They had been to the entrance more than once but, wisely, had refrained from entering without adult companions.

A small stream oozes down the steep side of the bowl-shaped sink-hole, dribbles into the cave, gathering more water from hidden springs as it flows on through the cavern; in spring the brook becomes a freshet and forms a tinkling waterfall just below the entrance and another far down inside. An ancient, rusted but still solid one-inch steel cable is fastened to a rock and dangles into the steep mouth which is paved with mud and leaves and pieces of wood, and with its assistance the descent is made fairly safe if not comfortable. There is a drop of fifteen feet or more to the floor of the cavern, with some long steps of rock which can be used by the agile spelunker to perform what mountain climbers call "chimneying" down, by the use of feet, knees, elbows and hands.

Once inside a world of wonders opens.

We are now walking along the solid floor of the cave, fifteen feet below the entrance. The eye is drawn irresistibly to look upward at the high, arching roof and the convoluted walls, which glisten as if sprinkled with gold dust or a combination of silver and gold, being covered everywhere with drops of water impregnated with calcium carbonate and colored by some other minerals, dissolved, such as iron. The effect is to provide an underground sky, dark as a rain cloud as to background but peppered with stars. To add to the miraculous scenic effect, in winter, hundreds of tiny bats hang all over the interior, and their fur has become covered with this same moisture with its golden sparkle, and the bats themselves, massed together or hanging singly here and there, become major stars in this subterannean firmament. This makes the cavern easily lighted by flashlights or carbide headlamps, and the reflections sometimes are so brilliant that it seems that light is coming from two or three directions at once.

The temperature is in the lower 50's at all times, and the atmosphere very humid. Warm clothing is necessary for comfort if a long stay is to be made, without continual activity. The cave at its deepest point, which is some 400 feet from the entrance, is 75 to 80 feet perpendicularly. Near the entrance on the right hand there rises a huge half-column of rock seeming to help support the roof, for it runs sheer up from the floor about 50 feet, and is perfectly half-round for most of its extent. Near it is a tent-shaped passage best described by the photograph which appears on another page.

The main passage is from six to ten feet wide, some of the floor heaped with fallen rock which is glued firmly together by the dissolved limestone and perfectly safe to scramble over, and there is the same natural cement holding the seemingly loose rocks in the roof and walls from dropping down. Those that have fallen probably became loosened in time of much rain or frost, and such periods are not the safest time to explore caverns; but the chances of a rock falling while one is in a limestone cave are so remote as to be practically negligible.

Indian Oven has its ups and downs along the main passage, with tempting opportunities for the young and eager to take the low road or the high road—and the very highest road of all is a maze of adits high up, close to the ceiling, to which some of the more adventurous spelunkers have clambered to scramble about, disappear, and reappear to the sight of those below.

There are not many of the usual cave formations to be seen in the main part of the cavern, no stalactites or stalagmites to be found, except in a part of the cave which is best described as the Attic Room. This is the usual first resting place for spelunkers, a great sloping mound of rock with a roof that slopes the same way above it and where a score or more of persons can stand, sit, or lie down. This is also a bat haven, in winter, the roof littered with the hibernating creatures, clinging upside down by their claws by the dozens, in groups and pairs and quintuplets. No official census has been taken of this bat colony but at times it is estimated that there are many hundreds here. Young people from Millerton sometimes come to collect bats for laboratory study and make a little money by their sale to institutions like Cornell University, where Dr. Donald R. Griffin, the famous "batologist," came in 1946 from Harvard Biological Laboratories to teach biology. Dr. Griffin had been banding bats in eastern New York State for ten years or more and often visited Indian Oven, himself. Many of the bands he has clipped about the elbows of these little brown bats are to be found among the colony now.[1]

Below the Attic Room, at the left, is a typical cave well, a round hole 6 to 8 feet deep, and leading off it, at the left, a small adit which leads to the lip of the carved limestone bed that was formerly the bed of a stream and the jumping-off place for the pretty waterfall.

It was near this waterfall, years and years ago, that a man named Holmes found his hunting dog, dead. The story is told as follows in the "General History of Dutchess County," by Philip H. Smith (Pawling, New York, 1877), pg. 249.

> About one hundred fifty rods from the west line of Northeast, in the town of Ancram, are the "Cave" and "Oven," two natural curiosities which attract numbers of visitors. The cave was discovered by a man named Holmes. He was hunting, and hearing his dog barking in a peculiar manner, he went up to him, but all he could see was a hole in the ground. Holmes pushed his dog into the opening, and went on, thinking the animal would soon follow; but he never returned. This excited some curiosity; and one day

[1]Dr. Griffin is the discoverer of what he calls *"echolocation,"* the capacity which bats have for avoiding flying into objects in total darkness, and which he applied to the assistance of blinded soldiers after World War II.

some young men went to examine the cave. They advanced a few feet, got frightened, and scrambled out as quickly as possible. They said they saw some barrels in the further end of the cavern, and heard strange noises, and believed it to be a den of thieves. Afterwards John Holley, Moses Dolph and John Culver, went into the cave, and at the farther extremity, found a spring and the remains of a dog. After this it was frequently visited.

About this time the State appointed some men to examine it, to determine its fitness for a prison, like one in Connecticut. They decided it was too damp to be used for that purpose.

The oven lies about eighty rods west of the cave. It is a piece of detached stone, and is so named from its shape, which resembles a large oven. A few years ago a geologist visited the locality; he gave it as his opinion that the oven was formed by the action of water.[2]

One must take with a little grain of salt the statement of the historian that the man named Holmes was so cruel and callous as to push his own hunting dog into a black hole in the rocks and go on his way without attempting to rescue the animal, but exactly the same thing is reported to have been done to bring about the discovery of the Twin Lakes Cavern at Taconic, Connecticut, not far from here, so perhaps it is true—or false in both cases. At any rate, only last summer, an unfortunate red fox fell or was chased into the Indian Oven Cave and its carcass lay on the floor at the foot of the entrance when a party of New England Grotto spelunkers explored the cave—mute testimony to the impossibility of an animal's escaping once it got down in there.

Indian Oven was the first cave that I ever visited in New York State and one of the first anywhere. I was introduced to this cavern in the autumn of 1935, on a wild week end of cave crawling which took me into six caves in two days and was the beginning of my long, long crawl into this "American Cave Series" of books. On this occasion the waterfall was working well, but an attempt to take a photograph of it failed; the camera lens had become fogged by the change in temperature

[2]This account furnished by courtesy of Mr. Gerald Carson, who has a small limestone cave on his own property that serves as a natural cooler or refrigerator.

from outdoors to inside. But the last visit, in June, 1946, found the waterfall sunk out of sight, and the narrow, intriguing passage which it had carved, and which was negotiable in 1935, was blocked at its upper end by a rock fall, evidently caused by the stream as it cut its way down.

This demonstration of the collapse of what might be called a cave within a cave is a splendid example of what the geologists say: that caves are all doomed sometime to die by committing suicide—although not in just those words.

There is another part of Indian Oven Cave into which not many persons have crawled. It might well be called the Worm Hole. It is at the extreme end of the Attic Room that the passage begins. Spelunkers whom I had guided to the cave, eight in number, entered this Worm Hole when told of it. It had first been explored, so far as can be learned, in March, 1939, by some boys who were members of a gala party of thirty-two persons who were on the hunt for the dread *Glawackus*.[3] Two of them were my sons. The passage is estimated to be about 100 feet long and not more than 3 feet high or wide at any point—but well supplied with large stalagmites firmly cemented to the floor and some hanging stalactites and masses of beautiful flowstone. The entrance had to be made over a hump at the Attic Room end, headfirst, and it took a full hour for the eight men and women led by Jack Butler, of Westfield, Massachusetts, and the Carson girls, Sally and Gay.

Fatigued by some considerable hiking and climbing about, I sat on a wooden box which one of the party had brought in with what I supposed was camera supplies.

As one after the other of the adventurers disappeared, their lights vanished, their voices also, here sat a lone caveman, his carbide lamp burning brightly as his only company, save for the curiously metallic sound of the buried waterfall coming up out of the deep well. There were no bats in the cave. They had all gone out for the summer. There was not even an insect crawling about. The splash and drip of the water, sounding

[3] (See *New England's Buried Treasure*, by Clay Perry.)

like an eaves-trough emptying into a tin cistern, became louder and louder, so it seemed. Looking up at the roof, idly, I noted inscriptions, "H.B.M.K.L.H." and "H.A.Beers, '08."

Ten minutes seemed a long time. Twenty minutes seemed an hour or more. Half an hour passed, and a chain of cigarettes had been smoked, some notes scribbled down, and the ears began to hear voices. The party must be returning. No, those were the voices of the hidden waterfall. Running water always has voices, out in the open or down in a cave.

Having rested, the lone caveman began to be restless and decided to move about. I was getting chilly, despite a thick woolen jacket and a heavy army field jacket over that. I started to crawl about, but as I did so my carbide light began to fail. It would be best to stay still and not go roaming about over the rocks and fall into a well or something, in the dark, not having developed a sense of echolocation.

The lamp, despite much shaking and adding of water from a bottle, faded down, down to no more than a match flame. Extra carbide was needed and that was in a knapsack which had been loaned to one of the party before entering and had been left on the ground outside. Lesson number one, to a supposedly well-trained spelunker: Always carry your carbide in with you, preferably in a pocket. Also, be sure to have an ordinary hand flashlight with you. That, also, had been left outside by the young lady to whom it was loaned, because she had been given a better light, an electric headlamp. Paper matches were plentiful, but no stub of a candle was in any of the usual pockets.

The light went out completely.

For probably fifteen or twenty minutes the lone caveman sat and smoked, watching the glowing tip of cigarettes, listening intently, watching for the appearance of a beam of light from the Worm Hole. The experience was a splendid demonstration of how it feels to be in solitary in total darkness—when the cigarettes go out. It does not feel nice at all. Even with the knowledge that eight merry, well-lighted spelunkers were only in the next room—but not to be heard or seen, until, finally, a faint, girlish giggle announced the returning party on its way.

The darkness-wrapped caveman began to grin at himself. The owner of that girlish giggle was going to have a laugh on him. Everyone had enjoyed one good laugh, as Mrs. Butler, coming down to the Attic Room, complained that it was pretty dark and she couldn't see where to place her feet. Someone turned and looked at her and said,

*"Why don't you take your dark glasses off?"*

Now, the caveman was to be laughed at for having no light—but he did not know the half of it, yet.

"What's the matter? No carbide?" he was asked when the Worm Hole explorers got out.

"That is exactly the trouble."

*"Well, you're sitting on it, in that box."*

## *Chapter II*

# HORSE-THIEF CAVES

FROM the lofty ledge which holds the Indian Oven Cave, the view to the east and northeast, across the valley of the Roeloff Jansen Kill Brook, is magnificent. The quiet, level, sometimes rolling prairie landscape of the valley has as its background the great, unbroken range of the Taconic Mountains, a bulwark between New York, Connecticut, Massachusetts, and Vermont, with few passes in the rocky wall. Far up at Hillsdale the ancient, now modernized turnpike that was built as the first road out of Massachusetts into New York State when George Washington was President, climbs up over Molasses Hill, crossing the line between the Empire State and the Bay State about one mile from where that boundary once was drawn, and where there was a tollgate. The old tollhouse still stands—or, rather, it leans dejectedly beside the concrete roadway.

At this point was literally the gateway between the two states, the old Columbia County Turnpike that once was a plank road. It joined the Salisbury Pike which ran through a picturesque pass, to the south, to the village of that name. What looks like a sort of a pass in the folds of the mountains over northeast of a tiny settlement, across the valley close to the rock wall, is a horse-thief trail.

Up in the Blow Hole is a horse-thief cave. The settlement which is glimpsed as a straggle of frame houses, a white church, a small, faded railroad station, and farmlands, is Boston Corner. It has been called Hell's Acres, with good reason, for in the middle of the nineteenth century it was the haunt of all manner of marauders, from thieves to prize fighters, from duelists to robbers and murderers. Hidden gold was once found in a hollow log in the woods, the unidentified plunder of some thief or band of thieves.

The strange story of Boston Corner and the horse-thief trail and cave is told in the historical novel, *Hell's Acres*.[1] That is, it is told, with novelists' license, so to speak, up to the autumn of 1853. What has happened since then is another story which needs no license to tell. Boston Corner, in 1853 and until 1855, was a part of Massachusetts. It was a district of the mountain top town of Mount Washington, Massachusetts. It was separated from its parent town so remotely by the mountain wall, however, that it had become a place "where there was no law, or none that could be enforced," in the language of a legislative commissioner who was sent to Boston Corner to report on its condition when the permanent inhabitants made their third urgent plea to become citizens of New York State, by cession of their village to the town of Ancram.

President Franklin Pierce issued in 1855 the proclamation which made the cession, and a little pie-shaped corner of just twelve hundred acres "of tillable and level land" was presented by this act to the Empire State—so that law could be enforced.

The trouble was that Boston Corner—so named perhaps because it was the farthest corner of Massachusetts from Boston itself—could be reached from Massachusetts only by the roundabout Molasses Hill road. Law officers, in attempting to get there to make arrests, had to travel for twelve miles through New York State, down the valley, thereby losing their authority.

There is no record that any arrests ever were made in Boston Corner by Massachusetts authorities, but there is plenty of evidence that many a felony was committed there and in the vicinity, including the spiriting of stolen horses up the rugged trail beside Black Grocery Brook, to a black rock gorge in the Blow Hole, and thence over the boundary line into Massachusetts.

It is really not a closed cave, this Horse-Thief Cave, so-called, but a narrow defile between cliffs of Berkshire schist and basaltic

[1]*Hell's Acres*, a historical novel, by Clay Perry and John L. E. Pell.

rock, mixed, which is one of the geological features of the Taconics. However, it served as a cave of sorts for the Black Grocery Gang, the rascals who ran valuable horses, colts preferred, stolen from the pastures and paddocks at Saratoga, up into the mountains, by way of this No Man's Land of Boston Corner.

The Black Grocery, incidentally, was not a grocery store at all. It dealt in wet goods, not dry goods. It was a notorious tavern of chestnut, unpainted, and weathered almost black, which stood alongside the Salisbury Pike midway between Boston Corner and Copake, long vanished, having burned down, with its proprietor inside. It was a fence for horse thieves, a place where stolen steeds were "painted" and otherwise doctored to change their markings and color, some of the best to be entered in races as "ringers" and thereby to make a double killing.

Boston Corner—which has been and still is erroneously called Boston Corners and Boston Four Corners, although there are not four corners in the place—is now a ghost town. It was originally a little industrial village with a fulling mill or two, a flour mill, some few houses. It became a boom iron-mining town in the 1880's or thereabouts and the old dumps and rotted tipples and grades of many a railroad track remain, grass-grown, to tell the tale of its decline. It was a heaven for horse thieves until 1855, as well as a resort for the plug-uglies who wished to hold what was a felony in every state save California, a prize fight. It was here in an open meadow, October 12, 1853, that John Morrissey of Troy and James "Yankee" Sullivan of London, Botany Bay, and Five Points on the Bowery, New York, fought the first heavyweight championship battle in the United States, but which is not so recorded in the annals of sport!

Perhaps it is because Morrissey was handed the decision by a crooked referee when he was beaten to his knees and choking with his own blood from the battering of the brine-pickled fists of the escaped convict, Sullivan. But that was the final event to cause the ceding of Boston Corner to New York State and the establishment of law and order in the valley of Black Grocery Brook—which is the locally preferred name for the Roeloff Jansen Kill Brook.

The horse thieves were finally eliminated by the vigorous pursuits made by "riders" of several anti-horse-thief associations, one of which still exists at Saratoga—as a social club—another in Dutchess County, or it did until a few years ago. This is a matter of history, although rather obscure history, that has been handed down through generations.

It is also history, not at all obscure, that the Anti-Renters who sought to escape the tolls exacted of them by the patroon landlords of eastern New York State, from Albany on down the line, fled through Boston Corner up to the seeming security of Mount Washington and were there established as early as 1690.[2]

Perhaps they fled by way of that horse-thief trail, through that black gorge, for that would be the shortest and only possible route save for the roundabout of Molasses Hill, and if they took that road they would be sure to be "squealed on" by the master of the gate, who was a sort of official in those days. At any rate, there is a well-defined old road up through the gorge of the Blow Hole, so named because it forms a veritable wind tunnel for the development of northeast gales into such tempests that the snow is piled up twenty feet deep in Boston Corner and, in the old days of small, flimsy railroad cars, they were blown off the track of the Harlem Line. The old road, however, becomes somewhat confusing as one climbs up the gorge of the Blow Hole, for much logging has been done along the range and forest fires have swept it many times and littered the rocky ground with down timber. But it can be followed up to an old clearing, just across the Massachusetts line where, tradition has it, the horse thieves sometimes pastured their four-footed booty while awaiting a chance to drive them to market for sale or to the race track to run against horses from the same stable they were "lifted" from, as "ringers." That is, they were

[2]See Chapter 12, "High and Low in the Helderbergs."

The author, below, and Richard F. Logan, geologist and leading speleologist, in Indian Oven Cave, Millerton, N. Y., seeking bats that hibernate there in large numbers

Cave Nymphs

The author, lost in Bentley's Cavern, Berlin, N. Y. for fifteen minutes

run in under false names and registry indicating them as slow horses.

The Horse-Thief Cave is a gorge, remember—but there is a true cave not far away which may have been mixed up in local legend with the gorge. It was, for many years, at least for half a century, believed to be a huge cavern with a large underground lake in it and the haunt of wild animals.

It is perhaps too bad that a party of Yankee spelunkers, who were also rather mischievious debunkers, should have shrunk that reputed big cavern into a tiny cavelet in the base of Alander Mountain, but they were and still are sticklers for facts. I was one of them, who went seeking to find that hidden, magnificent underground fairyland or wild animal zoo.

I had come upon a reference to it in Clark W. Bryan's *Book of Berkshire,* a guidebook published in 1885 and reissued in 1890. This supposedly factual and reputable guide referred to the cave as a big one, basing this conclusion upon the report that men or boys had "gone to the entrance and had felt drafts of cold air sweeping out and had seen the tracks of animals which had entered and left the cave."

The cold air was supposed to come from the big, deep lake that lay buried in the heart of Alander Mountain. Whether the wild animals were of a size commensurate with this tall tale of the cave, was not stated—but when the Yankee spelunkers-debunkers arrived on the scene, having been escorted to it by the superintendent of the Masters estate, on which the cave is located, they found . . .

"I can get in only about 12 feet with my clothes on," shouted Roger Johnson, Chief Spelunker of the New England Spelunkers' Club.

He had on hip boots, heavy sweater and old trousers. He was followed in by others, one of whom discovered a wild *moth.* It had reddish wings. It hung dormant on the wall above that great lake—a pool of water formed by a spring that trickled out instead of in, from a low, narrow passage in limestone.

"I am going to try to get in that passage and see where it

leads to," announced Roger and, emerging, he stripped to the skin although it was a cold November day. (The party was entirely male.) Crawling in like a bear in his bare skin, Spelunker Johnson, shivering and chattering, bumped his head against solid rock about 25 feet up the watery adit—and backed out, because he could not turn around and, after a brisk rubdown with a towel, dressed and set down in his ever-present notebook the fact that this Alander Mountain cavern was really a small and somewhat moth-eaten cave. It would not do to stable horses in, and even a horse thief would not feel small enough to inhabit it very long.

But there is a "Hot Hole Cave" high up on the side of Alander Mountain. Our guide, the superintendent, told us so, and declared that while out hunting foxes he came upon this hole, which was like the mouth of a chimney in the solid rock, and warmed his chilled hands with the heated air that came up from unknown depths. It was too small to enter and plumb its depth. Perhaps a warm spring may exist, down at the bottom.

The notorious Loomis Gang built a sort of cavern to conceal their stolen booty, harnesses, all sorts of equine equipment which they took, along with the many horses they stole and hid in their "impenetrable" Nine Mile Swamp in Cherry Valley.

The story has been often told, one way and another, as in *Body, Boots and Britches,* by Harold W. Thompson, in Carl Carmer's *Listen for a Lonesome Drum,* and in fictionized form by Harriet Doual Daniels in *Nine Mile Swamp.* The reputed man-made cavern connection is related by Carmer as a tag-end to his chapter on the gang.

One, Pop Risley, told him of an Irish peddler who stopped at Risley's gunsmith shop with some tinware and such goods and told how Plum Loomis, the youngest of the sons of the Wash Loomis family, led him to a rise of ground behind the old homestead site, "put his foot on a clod just under him . . . and a slab of land the size of a double barn door began to slide upwards and inwards and there was a hole big enough to drive a team o' horses and a surrey in and have room besides . . . soon as our eyes got used to the light I seen it was a cave as big as two carriage barns in one. And all around the outside walls was the prettiest gear I ever seen in my life. There was buggies and traps and coaches and surreys so black and shiny that the light they reflected from the big door behind us fair blinded our eyes. There was saddles with silver mountings and saddles with gold mountings. There was black harness and harness of a pretty light brown color and all the rings of it was polished silver and the check-reins hooked on silver hooks and there was special plates of silver on the blinders . . . It was a horseman's heaven. And when we come out Plum says, 'I don't need to tell you to say nothin' about this,' an' I says, 'No, ye don't need to tell me.' Then Plum steps on the clod again and the piece of hillside rolls in place, an' ye couldn't see where it joined on to the rest. Plum died a few months later an' nobody else knew about all that stuff bein' hid there. It's bound to be there yet and I want ye should go over there sometimes with me and help me find the clod to step on."

Pop says he said, "I've got to go on to Hubbardsville right now but I'll be back and then we'll both go over there and find that stuff."

"But he never came back," says Pop, "and I never believed any of his tarnation foolishness anyway."

Then there is the tale of a peddler—maybe the same one—who was seen entering the Loomis hideout—and never came out. Possibly he went back alone and got caught snooping around.

There was horse stealing all up and down the Taconic Range, extending into the wild fastnesses around the Stephentown and Alps village, high up in the mountains. One of the last bold thefts occurred in 1912 or 1913 when a notorious chicken thief named Williams, who spent most of his time in jail in Pittsfield, Massachusetts, suddenly turned horse thief, stole a splendid pair of draft horses, wagon and all, from the Shaker colony in West Pittsfield, and hit the pike over the steep Lebanon Mountain highway, leaving no trace until he got to Troy.

The late Daniel Flynn, who was chief of police in Pittsfield at the time and who had become well acquainted with the haunts and hideouts of the rascals who then lived or made temporary homes in the Alps section, picked up the trail at a "fence" in Troy, and found the harnesses and wagon in a barn in the Alps village vicinity, finally recovering the team as well and putting Williams back in jail. He had no cave to hide in, however, but plenty of woods and other sorts of hideouts in a section known for years as Woodchuck City, because the half-wild children of the hill-billy folks, wearing hair so long they looked like animals, would dive for shelter in a cellar window or any hole they found nearest, whenever strangers appeared along the turnpike.

The Alps-Stephentown-Hancock area was known infamously as being the haunt of thieves who preferred to "lift" young colts from pasture or paddock and spirit them away to Boston Corner or elsewhere. Somewhere in Stephentown, according to Robert Parker, a former resident of Pittsfield, whose veracity is unquestioned, there is a big cave in a mound of earth many yards long. We expect to explore it some day.

It is a very faint legend—perhaps more of an imaginative idea—that some of the Anti-Renters hid in caves along the border. There is no reference to this in the carefully documented but as yet unpublished history of the town of Mount Washington, which reposes in a little wooden box in the safe in the Town Hall in that lofty village, whither several families of Anti-Renters fled from the patroons of the Hudson Valley. In 1690 they were so well established that a census of farms, taken by the authorities of Massachusetts, listed the farms, inhabitants and numbers of barrels of "syder" in their cellars, and proved it the first settlement in Berkshire County, Massachusetts.

One of those families still lives there, in the fourth generation or so, named Spurr. It was Spoor, of the Hudson River Dutch clans. They, with others, had departed from their rented acres in Livingston Manor, were pursued by armed minions of the Livingstons, and one man, William Race, was shot and killed and got a mountain in the Taconic chain named after him.

The Anti-Renters were farmer tenants of the patroons who had received grants of vast area, either from the King of England or from the Indians, or both, and who gave leases to farmers, requiring certain payments in farm produce or money, which went on forever. No tenant could purchase his farm, and if the tolls or taxes were not paid, they accumulated so that many poor families lost their homes or were jailed. The anti-rent wars, so-called, went on for over a century, finally were settled by legislation in the middle of the nineteenth century.

## *Chapter III*

# BEARS' AND OTHER DENS

ON UP the northerly extension of the Taconic Range in North Stephentown and in Berlin are two caves, one of them with a main chamber, huger than any in this range, and second only to Howe Caverns. This is Bentley's Cavern, a short distance west of Berlin Center. It is owned by descendants of the original Bentley family, who settled here, a hundred years ago, beside the old post road to Troy. The family will direct spelunkers to the cave, which is about one mile due south of their home. It is not easy to find.

The other cave is the Bear's Den, yawning in the side of Butternut Hill on the farm of the late Charles B. Armsby, of Troy, and his brother. This cavern, also, is curiously elusive. One needs a local guide if he has not visited it before. Two parties of confident spelunkers, all rigged out, among them two who had visited it, were unable to find it again in half a day of roaming the wooded hill. This, despite the fact that the entrance is wide enough to admit a load of hay.

Bear's Den looks as if an explosion of rock had occurred in the hillside, hurling boulders and fragments out and down a very steep, long slope, forming a talus covering many square yards. The cave is concealed from the only negotiable portion of the hillside, under a ledge of one of the benches of the hill and with old fallen trees and growing bushes over the top and bushes making a further screen, but it can be walked into upright, and has a main chamber some 15 feet in diameter, roughly, and as high to the peak of the roof. At one side runs an adit that looks like an artificial tunnel but is not, extending perhaps 25 feet to a dead end. This cavern is perfectly dry and is a "dead" cave, with no formation of note formed or forming.

Its tall tales are many, two of them being pretty well authenticated, however. It was the home of a bear or bears at one time; then it became the hideout of white settlers who were afraid of the marauding Indians and would flee to this safety, where a grand view of the surrounding country is spread out in three directions, south, east and west.

Paul Braham, a white trapper, made it his refuge in the 1770's, when he thought Indians were after his hide because he was snaring beaver in their happy hunting grounds. This hideout was convenient to a spring which flows out of the ground, headwaters of Kinderhook Creek.

Braham liked the place so well that he built a log cabin near this spring which issues from under Eagle Rock. This location was selected not only because of the spring but because it was on the opposite side of the Butternut Hill ridge from an Indian village, and Braham had learned that the Indians did not know of the existence of the cave, which he could run to in a beeline if necessary. One, Daniel Hull, a pioneer, came from Redin, Connecticut, looking for Braham, left his oxen at Stephentown and was not seen again until twelve years later when "he returned for his oxen," as an account published in the *Troy Record* in 1934 has it, from an interview with Charles Armsby.

"The last bear shot in that vicinity," this same account continues, "was brought down by a ball from the rifle of John Barney Straite, about 1912, and the rifle was placed in the collection of Dr. Alson J. Hill of Troy, who was preparing a museum of antiques from the Berlin Mountains."

The Armsby family transformed a sugar-bush into a pretty picnic ground, and for years it was visited by a group of gourmets from Troy, who enjoyed clambakes and barbecue feasts beneath the tall trees and the shadowing ledge of Eagle Rock.

In those times a good private road led to the spot, running right between the farmhouse and barn. It was negotiable by automobile, but it is now better to walk. Be sure to get a good local guide. Some small boy in the vicinity will know of Bear's Den.

Most of the "wild caves" of the east are coy about themselves, it seems. They are very well hidden, in remote spots on mountain sides or summits, at the base of a hill, somewhere in the woods or a neglected portion of a farm; and no written directions to many of them are sufficient to steer a novitiate to the entrances. Nature conspires, also, to change her complexion in an astonishingly short time, so that even from one year to another the landscape becomes strange to previous visitors to these wild areas.

Bentley's Cavern in Berlin is a very good example of a well-concealed cavern. One can—and some have—passed by the entrance within a few yards and not recognized it, after having entered it at least once. It is "over behind that hill" from the Bentley homestead and there are two rough trails by which it can be reached. You are on your own after getting local directions; you can take either trail and get lost, or lose the cave; but some woodcraft and persistence, coupled with careful notations about landmarks, should enable any true spelunker to find it. It is a hike of a mile or so, not much more, by either trail. One is steeper than the other. THE LEFT HAND trail is the better one, and it does not become a trail until a barren pasture on a hillside has been crossed, a hillside out of which oozes spring water that flows, or used to flow, into a roadside watering tub. Landmark number one.

Circling to the left of the hill, the trail faintly shows through thin woods, up a gradual rise, through hollows grown to grass and brush, passing a huge old maple tree just beyond a barbed-wire fence at the right. Hugging the base of the hill, one comes to a sort of gorge, with cliffs on each side, open at each end, and a pool of black water in the sinkhole. Cattle keep it stirred up. It seems to have no inlet, but it does have springs and it probably seeps down very slowly and becomes an underground stream in the cave.

The entrance is in the side of the taller cliff, above the pool; there are two of them, one a "chimney" which thrusts down past the lower entrance. In either case it is a "jackknife" entrance, requiring some expert "chimneying" to get in; whereupon one is in a roomy, high-roofed, tunnel-like chamber with immediate beautiful formations on all sides. There is considerable crystalline limestone just beyond the dark, weather-stained rock opening you have squirmed through; and one formation is a glittering, gigantic hood into which a man can back and sit down and seem to be wearing a Titanic helmet of sparkling jeweled interior. This is the most beautiful and unusual formation in the cavern. The tunnel leads on, up and down, the floor of jumbled and cemented rocks, filled in with the dessicated limestone which when wet is as slippery as soap—and then suddenly the stand-up tunnel ends and there is a 50-foot creeping tunnel to negotiate.

Here is where the brook appears, a very shallow one in normal season, not more than 1 to 2 inches deep, its bed of solid rock, plus scattered stones and a number of old boards and poles that have been dragged in, somehow, so that the spelunker can wriggle over them on his belly, elbows, knees and toes, headfirst, and not get completely soaked.

At the end of this wet crawl is a small vestibule, a room with hanging "wings" of water-carved limestone, coming very close to the slippery earthen floor, but not half bad after emerging from the wet-crawl tunnel. This leads into the main chamber—and here is a real surprise.

This chamber is large enough to hold a regiment of soldiers or a national cave convention crowd. It looks something like an underground stadium, with a sloping bank of slippery, coated rocks, from the ever-present decayed limestone that has formed a substance like modeling clay, and which was once "mined" from this cave to become the base for a rather crude sort of paint, with which the neighboring residents used to smear their barns, adding a pigment to color it red.

One of my visits, and there have been three of them, to Bentley's Cavern, provided both a frightening and a comic experience. There were two of us—there always should be at least two on a cave-exploring expedition—Arthur Palme, Pittsfield,

Massachusetts, photographer of all outdoors and much indoors, in caves, dragging, pushing, and pulling his little suitcase with his camera and equipment in it. We were awed at the size of this great chamber, which I think is the very largest single room as to length, width, and height in New York State's undeveloped caves.

Soon we were impelled to attempt to clamber up that stadium bank which might be carved into tiers of seats. As it is, the slope is a greasy, difficult climb. As we started up, keeping close to one wall, our flashlights suddenly revealed a skull, glaring from empty eye-sockets, perched upon a pedestal, elevated a few feet above the floor, on a boulder.

Visions of the raid that was once made upon a gang of gamblers that used to frequent this retreat to participate in day-and-night-long games of chance, of some sheriff shooting his way through an attack by the ruffians, were soon dissipated, for *the skull had been modeled from the clay of the cave* by some skillful hands and deliberately placed where it would confront the first person to try to climb those slippery stairs.

We decorated this empty bone-head with a used flash-bulb and giggled and went scrambling on up, up, until we could get no farther, heads against the roof, where bats hung in imitation of large brown grapes.

An hour later, having explored all we thought was negotiable of the cave, including a washed-boulder brook bed, which later we were told could be squirmed down a long way, we prepared to make our exit. It was getting along toward the setting time of the sun, it was autumn and cool. We had many miles to drive to get home. Palme pushed his little suitcase with its precious contents, including some flash-bulb photos of the cavern, into a tiny hole in the wall of the big chamber.

"Say, I can't get through here!" he yelped, in a muffled voice. "A rock has fallen down since we came in!"

"Why, are you sure?"

He backed out, pulling his suitcase after him and said he was darned sure.

"Let me try it; I can't believe . . ."

My flashlight showed me that there *was* a rock sticking down in that tunnel, within 3 or 4 inches of the floor, Not even a woodchuck could have got past it. And it was solidly fixed there. It simply could not have fallen down since we came in.

We went into a huddle, literally and mentally, with some secret side glances at the skull—and I remembering that my name was Clay and might be "mud." We lit cigarettes and threw our flashlight beams about here and there and calmed down. Oh, we were very calm, indeed—and then suddenly one of us remembered that we had *come through a vestibule room.*

It would have been very romantic and dramatic had it happened that the bats had begun to fly out for their suppers—but these were hibernating bats who would not eat until spring, so we had no "guides with wings," my fiction story with that title in *Boys' Life Magazine,* published later, notwithstanding; but it was based on fact.

We crept meekly through the vestibule room and into the wet-crawl tunnel and came out just before it was dark. It was wonderful to breathe in the crisp fall air of the great outdoors. The Bentleys, when we reported at the house, were glad to see us; they had not wished to muster a rescue party.

Bentley's Cavern was once a den of thieves, cloth thieves who were reputed to steal good woolen cloth from a Berlin mill and hide it here. It was, as aforesaid, also a den of gamblers, men who were so wedded to their sport that they had a veritable cave gambling club, with a giant Negro posted at the entrance to give warning if law officers appeared.

It is local history—or legend—that this band of gamesters would remain in the cave, squatting on the dry floor of the great chamber, for days and nights, having brought in with them food and drink. But the Negro guard, it is related, became so proud of his position that he bragged about it, and one dull, blue morning as the red-eyed gamesters appeared out of the jackknife entrance above the black pool, the sheriff was there with his posse and the gaming was broken up.

Whether the sheriff or one of his posse placed that grisly model of a skull inside as a warning or memento, is something to think about—but it is no longer there. Someone has kicked it to pieces or removed it.

If you drive on to Troy there is a noted Counterfeiters' Cave to be visited. En route is a cavern which A. Douglas Schleif, of Stephentown Center, who owns the property where it is located, says had not been explored in twenty-five or thirty years. Some venturesome persons let themselves down a shaft in the top of a hill, several rods east of N. Y. 66, about midway between Denault's Corners and Hoag's Corners, into a roomy series of chambers. These persons, now old men, declared that they traveled far enough westerly in the cave that they could hear the beat of horses' hoofs on the highway above their heads.

On the grounds of the Troy Country Club, off Brunswick Road, is a Counterfeiters' Cave of curious history, most of which is furnished by Carl S. Hulett, Jr., Editor of the *Chatham* (N. J.) *Courier,* a former resident of Troy.

It is a small cave, really quite insignificant as far as caves go, he says, but fairly well known in that locality. It is on the south bank of Poestenkill Creek, just a few yards from the bridge crossing the creek as it flows through the property of the Country Club. The entrance is a narrow slit in the rocks and one must lie prone to wriggle into an underground room, approximately 6 feet high, 3 feet wide, and 7 feet long.

The roof of the cave slopes sharply at one end, and it is at this point, "according to legend," that a passage starts which leads several hundred yards under the creek's bed to the opposite shore.

Mr. Hulett admits that in his youth he tried to excavate inside the cave to find this passage but failed, but that "old timers swear that there is such a passage and some claim to know the exit on the opposite shore and to have actually journeyed through the passage."

No reference to this cave can be found in local histories, but it has been popularly known as Counterfeiters' Cave, a hideout for these manufacturers of the "queer," and the story is that at one time a considerable amount of fake money was found in the cave. Another story is that early settlers used the cave and passage as a refuge or escape from hostile Indians.

The geological features of the Troy area are such as to make it very possible there might be one or more sizeable or extensive caverns in the region, but not very probable, for it is estimated that in ages past the area was covered with a mass of ice 2,000 feet thick, and that the terrain was crushed and ground and shifted as the glacial mass moved.

There are many outcrops of olive shales in Troy, found in the limestone-breccia ledges, one near Oakwood Cemetery which contains a vein of quartz crystals which were revered by the Indians as "spirit stone," and which the English settlers called "diamond rock."

Some of the great boulders of the glacial drift may be seen along the Brunswick Road and Stone Road in the bed of the Deepkill, north of the city.

Other interesting cavernous formations are the Devil's Chimney near the Fallen Hill in Old Schagticoke and Hoosick Pass.

There is a faint chance of a cave in the little village of Garfield, called Diamond Cave, and supposedly named after the Diamond family from which sprang the gangster, "Legs" Diamond, who did have a hideout in the hills in this vicinity at one time, but evidently he kept this a deep, dark secret, if he used a cave to hide in. No trace of it could be found in a survey of the territory or by inquiry from local residents, but it is a goal worth seeking for spelunkers with do-or-die instincts.

## *Chapter IV*

# MUSEUM PIECES

For the tenderfoot who may wish to go spelunking without bothering with rough clothing and heavy equipment, there are caves in at least three museums in New York State. Most convenient to the millions of Gotham are two rebuilt caverns in the American Museum of Natural History, New York City. They are not York State caves. They are imported and installed in the mineralogy department, one from Virginia, one from Arizona.

But while we are in the north country, let us by all means first visit the historic citadel of Fort Ticonderoga. In its marvel of a museum of antiquities there is a cave which has been restored and placed in a glass case, with the bones of a gigantic caveman who inhabited it and lay himself down to die or was entombed by members of his tribe. On his body and in his hands had been placed some of his most precious and sacred possessions, artifacts of a prehistoric race. This caveman was an early Algonquin Indian, who was 6 feet 10 inches tall, as established by bone measurements.

The whole story is told in the *Bulletin of Champlain Valley Archeological Society* for December, 1937, Vol. 1, No. 1. This was made available to us by Mr. Stephen H. E. Pell, owner of Fort Ticonderoga, and Mr. Milo S. King,, superintendent of the fort and secretary and treasurer of the society. This complete and careful account is titled "A Rock Shelter at Fort Ticonderoga," and was written by John H. Bailey, archeologist.

As this bulletin is out of print and we are privileged to have the very last available copy, it seems desirable to reprint herewith a generous portion of the account, for which we have permission, and we quote:

Sentinel Rock, at the tip of the point of land upon which Fort Ticonderoga stands, has long been used as a watch tower because of its strategic situation, enabling an observer to have a clear view both up and down Lake Champlain. As such a post it was used during the French and Indian Wars and American Revolution, and it is only natural that years before the white man came, the American aborigines should have adopted the terrace beneath as a home and an ideal spot from which to watch for the advance of their enemies.

Those who visit Fort Ticonderoga may discover with their own eyes what a magnificent lookout the aborigines discovered and used by asking to be guided to the rampart of the Grenadiers' Battery, which overhangs exactly the site of the Indian Rock Shelter.

After starting abruptly at a height of about fifteen feet above the water, the ground level rises by two terraces to end at the foot of a cliff of Beekmantown limestone which towers twenty-seven feet above the floor of the shelter as shown in Diagram 1. Each of these terraces, the rock shelter floor resting on the second, is strewn with large blocks of limestone, presumably weathered from the cliff above or the rock face supporting the upper terrace. The topsoil on the lower terrace contains many small fragments of limestone, a few chips of chert, small fragments of animal bone and an occasional sherd of pottery.

The rock shelter proper extends along the foot of the cliff for a distance of approximately thirty feet with a refuse accumulation averaging two feet six inches at the back wall and thinning out gradually as the edge of the terrace is reached. The surface was found to be covered with large blocks of limestone, all of which had presumably dropped from the projecting ledge which is continually weathering away. The ground level rises quite rapidly at the southern end of the shelter as the terrace widens with a steep rocky slope. At the northern end, the surface descends and widens as it reaches the level of the lower terrace.

The shelter was discovered in September 1936 by several members of the Champlain Valley Archaeological Society and subsequently excavated by them. The writer desires to take this opportunity to express his appreciation of the cooperation given him by the members who assisted in the excavation of this shelter and who, by sharing their knowledge of the place, made possible this report.

The shelter was formed by a projecting layer of limestone which extends for a maximum distance of four feet at the present time from the supporting rock wall and to some extent covers about eighteen feet of the floor. This is not a very large area of protecting overhang at present, but was evidently enough for the aboriginal inhabitants of the shelter at the time of their occupancy. The refuse mantle rested on an uneven sub-floor layer of clay through which many large rocks projected. The floor consisted of an almost homogeneous layer, containing large fragments of limestone, small chips of limestone, chips of chert and quartzite from the manufacture of arrowpoints, some small sherds of pottery, mussel shells, and several hundred fragments of bone. Among the mammals represented are the bear, deer, woodchuck, beaver, chipmunk, red squirrel, weazel, porcupine, fox, lynx, dog and muskrat.[1] In the bird class, we find turkey and duck bones, while the fish diet is represented by the jaws, vertebrae and spines of such fishes as the bullhead, trout, gar and other unidentified species. The presence of the turtle was shown by the fragments of the carapaces and plastrons of at least two specimens. With the exception of a partial skeleton of a horse and several cow vertebrae probably thrown from the ledge above and found practically on the surface of the shelter, all the bones found can be attributed to the Indian occupants and were more or less evenly distributed over the floor of the shelter both horizontally and vertically.

Approximately under the remaining maximum overhang and at a depth of one foot two inches, there was uncovered the skeleton of an adult male about 55 years old. (See Diagram 2.) He had been buried in a loosely flexed position on the rocky floor and surrounded by large weathered slabs of the cliff material set on edge with their flat surfaces sloping outward from the grave, forming, with the wall of the shelter, a saucer-shaped depression. The body had been placed on its back headed southwest and presumably facing northeast, although the decaying of the body and subsequent settling of the ground had detached the skull from the skeleton, leaving it caught under a large rock which had probably been placed over it at the time of burial. (See Plate I.) The knees had been flexed to the right with the left hand over the breast, while the right hand had been folded back on the right shoulder.

[1]The writer desires to take this opportunity for expressing his appreciation to Dr. Dayton Stoner of the State Museum, Albany, N. Y., for valuable assistance in identifying many of the mammal bones.

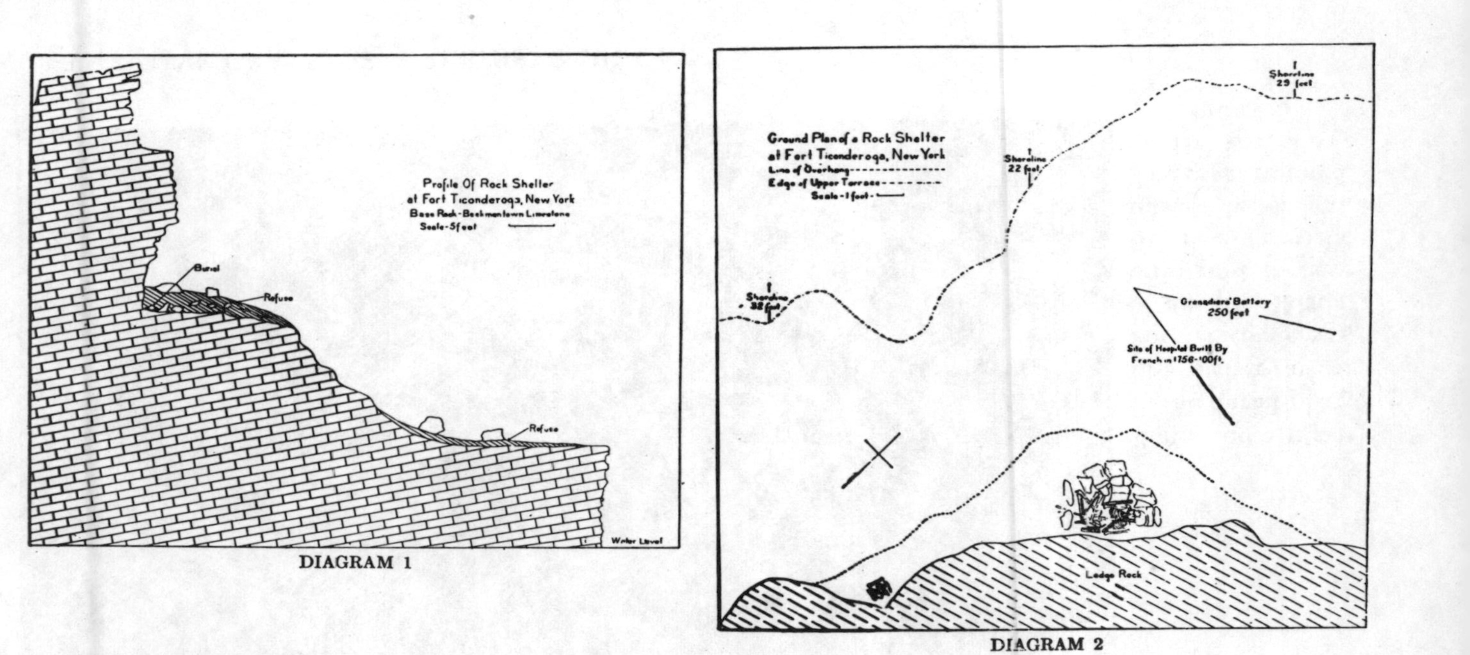


Sketches of the Indian Cave Grave at Fort Ticonderoga

Bones and artifacts in the burial place, in a shelter cave at Fort Ticonderoga, of an early Algonquin said to have been 6 feet 10 inches in height. The cave, restored, is in the Fort museum

THE CAVE GRAVE OF A PREHISTORIC GIANT

Over the breast bone, or sternum, two antler pitching or flaking tools were encountered. These are the only objects which might be safely called "grave goods" or articles intentionally placed with the burial, and although one notched arrowpoint of local black chert was discovered among the rocks surrounding the burial it may be a purely accidental inclusion. Over the left hip bone were several ribs, and beneath these were the ulnae and radii constituting the fore legs of a black bear. Extending along the vertebral column was a mass of fish bones, perhaps a burial offering of food.

Beneath the leg bones of this burial and scattered through the refuse mantle in the surrounding area, were found fragments of the skeleton of a child about seven years of age. The bones of the child's feet were in articulative order beneath the leg bones of the adult, although the rest of the infant skeleton was scattered in fragments nearby. Many of the pieces of the child's skull show evidence of having been gnawed by small rodents and the supposition is that while preparing a grave for the adult, the child's grave was found, partially removed, and scattered on the shelter floor where the skull fragments were found by rodents during a temporary abandonment of the shelter.

The pathology of the adult skeleton is discussed by Dr. Ralph Pamberton in a later section of this monograph.

Skeletons in a fine state of preservation are exceedingly rare on known aboriginal sites in the Champlain Valley. We probably owe the fine condition of this skeleton to the sheltered position where it was found and the charcoal, ash and limestone content of the refuse in which it had been buried.

From a pocket in the refuse soil under a small opening in the shelter wall (See Diagram 2) there was excavated a group of objects consisting of a hafted beaver-incisor engraver; nine deer antler tines, three of them worked; a bone awl; a small antler flaking tool; a stone adze; a stone implement in process of manufacture; and many fragments of split and cut animal bone. . . . Practically under this cache of objects, a few inches toward the edge of the shelter, was found the partial skeleton of an immature raccoon.

Between the burial and the cache of implements, there were said to have been several areas which appeared to have been used for a particular purpose. One of these consisted of a section covered with chips of chert and quartzite, a scraper, drill and rejects of blue-black local chert. Evidently here had been an arrowpoint maker's work shop. Another location contained a mass of fresh water clam shells, while a third, within a few feet of the grave, appeared to be a small hearth containing layers of charcoal and ash, a bilaterally shallow barbed harpoon, a fishhook of bone, and a fragment of a burned antler chisel.

The artifacts have been treated in groups, namely: antler and bone, chipped stone, polished stone, and pottery.

As a museum piece, the Sterlingbush Crystal Grotto, a rebuilt cave in the New York State Museum, Educational Building, Albany, stands out as perhaps unique in the entire world. It is one of the most beautiful things of its sort in this country. Here, in the hollow of a large square box buttress in the southwest corner of the Mineral Room of the Museum, behind glass, is a rebuilt cavern or grotto with countless semi-transparent calcite crystals forming its glowing walls, roof and floor. Under electric lights these crystals, large and small, glow like jewels, in violet, rose, and pink tints, in what appears to the eye to be a crawlable twisting tunnel some 30 or 40 feet in extent.

The story of this Crystal Grotto is told in brief in a plaque on the wall near the cave.

The grotto here reproduced in part was discovered by the members of the museum staff in 1906, in a limestone quarry at Sterlingbush, Lewis County, New York. It was detected as a small hole about four feet square on the quarry face, 20 feet above the floor. On entering with the aid of ladders and staging the cave was found to extend for a length of about 40 feet, expanding in width for a part of the distance but soon pinching out. The walls of this grotto were studded with crystals, most of them of immense size, wonderful perfection and of extraordinary violet and rose color —*a display of which it is safe to say the world has never shown the like.*

These crystals are calcites or lime-carbonate of exact geometric shape whether large or small. The largest weighs 1000 pounds; the small ones which encrust the spaces between the larger have only faint tints of color.

The grotto was destroyed in the quarry operations, but 12 tons of its crystals were removed.

This exhibit constructed with the original crystals, affords some conception of the extraordinary beauty of the place.

## ORIGIN OF THE GROTTO

The cavity was probably filled during long ages with waters saturated with lime carbonate, out of which the crystals were slowly built up. This grotto has been reconstructed by Noah T. Clarke and Charles P. Heidinrich.

Noah T. Clarke is a son of the late John M. Clarke, and is now archeologist at the Museum.

Some of the twelve tons of crystals brought to the Museum have been placed on stands in the mineral room, one huge one weighing half a ton. As a demonstration of what nature can do by its secret, subterannean chemical processes, the Crystal Grotto is undoubtedly one of the most striking things in the world. It is certainly totally unlike any cave formation known in America. Not even the very beautiful caverns of Virginia, New Mexico, and other states famous for their cave country, can show such a glowing display as this.

Here is a little secret about the reconstructed grotto. It isn't 30 or 40 feet long. They do it with mirrors. But you cannot see the mirrors and you seem to see a long cavern.

And now, turning away and walking out of the mineral room, easterly, we find that this Museum also has a mastodon cave! Complete with its mastodon, indeed, two of them, one a skeleton of the real animal and the other a reconstruction of it with all its long hair on. A third mastodon skeleton comes from another excavation.

Behind these great, prehistoric beasts on their pedestals, their great tusks curving like giant's scimitars, is a model of the caves in which the mastodon bones were found, four score years ago. The caves are really potholes, and they were broken into by workmen excavating for the foundation of the Harmony Mills at Cohoes in September, 1866.

The lower jaw and a single footbone were found on a ledge of rock on the side of a pothole, and continued excavations revealed the principal parts of the skeleton at a lower level of the same pothole, and in February, 1867, a few other bones in a smaller pothole about 60 feet to the southwest of the larger one.

To quote an excerpt descriptive of the Cohoes Mastodon *from New York State Bulletin 241-242,* "The Mastodons and Mammoths and other Pleistocene Mammals of New York State," by C. A. Hartnagel and S. C. Bishop, 1922, pages 10-11:

> Most of the bones were lying on a bed of clay and broken slate above a layer of waterworn pebbles. Above the bones there was an accumulation of muck, peaty soil with fragments of limbs and rotten, beaver-gnawed wood and artificial fill, almost 60 feet in thickness.
>
> The surface of the rock in which the potholes were excavated lies at a level almost 100 feet above the present surface of the river bed below the Cohoes falls. Hall[5] thought the potholes had been formed by the action of surface waters falling through crevasses in the ice sheet to the rock beneath but this interpretation has been generally abandoned in favor of the theory that they are of a post-glacial origin. Quoting H. L. Fairchild, O. P. Hay[6] states that at the time of the withdrawal of the ice sheet, the site of Cohoes was depressed about 350 feet below the present level and covered with a thick deposit of sand and clay laid down in the bed of Lake Albany. With the elevation of the land, Lake Albany was drained and the ancient Mohawk (Iromohawk) cut through the deposited sands and clays, reached bedrock and drilled the potholes.
>
> Various theories have been advanced to account for the presence of the skeleton in the potholes. Hall not only provided a glacial origin for the holes but for the mastodon itself which he believed to have been entombed in the glacier, dismembered by action of the ice and dropped, part in one pothole and part in another.
>
> Clarke[7] was of the opinion that the skeleton belonged to the period of swamps which covered the area after the fall of the post-glacial waters. O. P. Hay[8] stated his opinion as follows: "We may fairly assume that it (the mastodon) had only recently died and was lying on the flood plain not far above the potholes. No disarticulated bones could have been distributed as this skeleton was.

[5]N. Y. State Cab. Nat. Hist. 21st Annual Rep't, 1871, p. 105.
[6]Science 1919, 49:379.
[7]N. Y. State Mus. Bul. 69, 1903, p. 930.
[8]Science 1919, 49:379.

The bones must, perhaps without exception, have been held together by ligaments and probably much of the flesh remained. At this moment the river rose and swept the flood plain carrying the cadaver over the potholes.

It is certain that the skeleton was deposited long after the potholes had been drilled, for the majority of the bones rested on a bed of clay and broken slate above a layer of water-worn pebbles and gravel at least 10 feet thick. Above the bones the muck and peat deposit was at least 50 feet thick. It would seem therefore that the bones were deposited while in the flesh in potholes which were abandoned except at periods of high water, and subsequently covered by the accumulated debris of years.

The rebuilt caves in the American Museum of Natural History, New York City, serve to give the visitor to the mineralogy department a very good idea of different sorts of caverns from widely separated parts of the country, and they serve well to demonstrate that no two caves are alike.

The Arizona Cave was dug up and reconstructed by E. O. Hovey from the Queen Hill Workings of the Copper Queen Consolidated Mining Company at Bisbee, Arizona. The formations are tinted with varied colors, the green being due to salts of copper, the rose to manganese; the yellow and brown stains are from salts of iron, and the combination of formations and colors are typical of southwestern caves.

Weyer's Cave comes from the town of Grottoes, Virginia, and was once a part of what today is called Grand Caverns. This small section of a vast cavern, natural as it is, is quite illustrative of the numerous Shenandoah Valley caverns. There are several other cave formations in the mineral rooms, collected from many parts of the country, some from New York State, some from New England. An exhibit of these was prepared and put on display in November, 1946, under the direction of Miss Katharine Beneker, Director of Special Exhibitions, upon the occasion of publication of the first volume in "The American Cave Series," *New England's Buried Treasure*. The New England specimens and some of the New York State pieces were gathered by the author. It was also displayed at the Carnegie Museum in Pittsburgh and other eastern museums.

*Chapter V*

# NATURAL STONE BRIDGES AND CAVES

## CAUTION
## AT YOUR OWN RISK

So READS a small sign on a tree at the approach to the huge gorge at the Adirondack Natural Stone Bridge and Caverns, at Pottersville, which is near Schroon Lake, tucked away in a most natural, native, unspoiled little patch of woods and country just far enough from any main-traveled highway to be a restful place, and not at all a tawdry tourist attraction. Not that other so-called commercial caves are tawdry, in New York State, but some others are. There are just too many tourists and tin cans, waste paper, scattered pickles and mustard, souvenir stands, and ruthless souvenir-hunters who grab and gouge off anything they can find to carry away.

Everything about this Natural Stone Bridge and Caverns is natural, including its youthful proprietor, Miss Lydia Neubuck, who is its chief guide. This charming young lady in her early twenties is one of the principal attractions of the place, and the attractions are many and gorgeous.

Here is a gorge, a huge stone bridge and numerous caverns which have been carved out by furious, rushing water, ice-jams and log-jams, with a history of human interest dating back to the 1790's. Its geological history is the oldest in the Adirondacks.

It was formed in the Pre-Cambrian sedimentary rock, metamorphosed—a banded Grenville crystalline limestone. Many deposits of quartz, muscovite mica (white mica, commonly called isinglass) calcite, galenite, graphite, iron ore, and hornblende are prevalent. It is somewhat of a mineral collector's paradise of these geological mixtures.

The stream which carved its way through this conglomeration of rocks and minerals started out of small Hewitt Pond, to the northwest, as Minerva Creek, but after being supplemented by a branch brook from the north, became known as Trout Brook, and it winds up by emptying into the Schroon River and thereby becomes a part of the headwaters of the Hudson. At times this pretty creek or brook becomes a torrent, the water rising 20 feet in spring freshets, and it is a spectacular sight at the bridge and gorge and the caverns as the roaring flood rips through, and as there is always a great accumulation of ice and snow in the Adirondacks in winter, there is a big show in spring.

The Natural Stone Bridge, itself, is a great arch of rock that rises 62 feet above the stream-bed, is 180 feet across the span, and 1,000 feet wide from where the water flows under the arch to where it reappears, making it probably the widest natural structure of its sort in New York State and one of the widest in the country. Geologists find that great boulders in the stream-bed were brought down from Canada during the glacial period, the earliest importations of minerals from that country.

The earliest settlers of this north country came here about 1794 and began to log off the woods, floating their timber down the stream. At the waterfalls above the bridge are the remains of an old sawmill which was in working condition until forty-five years ago, at which time a huge dam was extended across the stream above the bridge to keep the logs from passing under it and getting into a jam; and nature had provided a natural sluiceway at the side of the bridge, a deep gorge with walls of solid rock. It was an ideal arrangement for the lumbermen—until, one year, the high water and ice-jams crashed the dam down and the logs went hurtling under the bridge.

In this breakaway, two loggers in a bateau, attempting to break up a jam, were carried in under the stone arch which becomes low bridge at about 100 feet in, and only by lying down flat in the tossing, whirling boat did they escape having their brains knocked out. They came safely through the 1,000-foot passage, but the logs jammed; and every year thereafter that logs were run down the stream, more joined them, and the passage is now solidly corked up by masses of logs, tree trunks, and other timber. Attempts are being made to remove them so that the stream passage will be clear and a fascinating underground boat ride can be afforded—in low water, not in spring.

It is with a feeling of awe and "caution at your own risk" that one approaches the brink of the cliff which is the upper side of the bridge, rising so high above the stream and its rock-strewn bed below, but so far no one has tumbled over the edge, and when a small girl five years of age can guide parties about the maze of gorges and caverns, the risk does not appear to be very great.

There are nine or a dozen curious and interesting formations here, ranging from potholes to caves of good size. The power of running water and rolling stones has ground out numerous potholes, the largest known as Indian Maid's Kettle. The caves have been named for their principal characteristics, such as Echo Cave, which extends some 60 feet into the rock and which can be visited only by swimming in or taking a boat ride. Geyser Cave spouts a veritable geyser against its own ceiling, in high water, and normally the water is 12 feet deep and flows underground some 25 feet in the cave before it vanishes.

Noisy Cave is the largest and most spectacular one, into which one may walk for 18 feet and look far back into where four waterfalls cascade from high crevices. This cavern opens into Peter Pan's Pothole, an inverted kettle extending 40 feet above and with a lofty balcony where the venturesome can lean over the edge and look down into Noisy Cave—so named because the cascades make a great clatter. As one writing man who visited it observed, "a very fine cave to go into with your wife if she is too garrulous." Above this great hole is Arch Rock, another small natural bridge, underground, and nearby, the Devil's Slide, a long tunnel that drops 100 feet from the top of the big bridge to its entrance—and only the devil in a hurry to get home would like to take the slide.

Most beautiful and unusual of all are the watery caverns off the gorge, below the ridge, one of them named Garnet Cave because of the garnets to be seen in its ceiling.

It was in the gorge and its side caves that a party of New England spelunkers made the first tryout of special equipment for negotiating underground waters, using an inflatable rubber boat of the Navy life-raft type, and Navy submersible rubber suits, also bathing suits for venturesome swimmers and divers. Garnet Cave opens off the gorge with a 10-foot-wide entrance, the water being 12 feet deep here; but as one gets inside, a ledge and boulders here and there provide places to stand on, and at its extreme end, which is 85 feet from the entrance, the water is shallow.

A unique feature of Garnet Cave was discovered by the Yankee spelunkers, lead by Roger Johnson of Springfield, Massachusetts, who had furnished the naval equipment, but who swam in and, without benefit of flashlight or candle, discovered a small water cavern opening off Garnet Cave 30 feet in. While resting on a rock that lay under the water he began to see a strange amber glow at the end of this cave. Realizing that the glow must come through the water from the bright July sun outside, he took a chance, and "did a reverse Casteret,"[1] as he expressed it, diving down under the rock and coming out in the open pool of the gorge. After several others had experienced the odd display of amber light—which it took some minutes to see at all, because the pupils of the eyes were so narrowed by the sun outside—it was decided to christen the find the Amber Grotto.

The tryout of the boat and suits proved highly successful, and they were used with excellent results at the New England Spelunkers' Grotto cave convention, held July 14, 1946, at the Strickland Feldspar Quarry, Portland, Connecticut.

It is possible to take your spelunking in the open air, in the water, which is at about 76 degrees Fahrenheit in mid-summer,

[1]Norbert Casteret was the French cave explorer who found prehistoric drawings and statues in a cave by diving through a dangerous siphon, trusting he would emerge in an open cave. He did.

inside and outside, or to clamber about on rustic steps and bridges in and through the various caverns. A hike up the brook through the woods is an "added attraction" to help whet the appetites for a picnic lunch under the evergreens on the grounds.

The property which Miss Neubuck and her mother operate came to Lydia from a great-uncle who farmed and logged here and whose farm was the last one at the very end of an ancient roadway, branching off from U. S. 9 near Pottersville. Pay no attention to forbidding signs at the gateway of this road or along it, for they are merely the expression of the desire of a nearby property owner to keep people from enjoying themselves at the Natural Stone Bridge and Caverns. The other signs are welcome signs, directing you to the 275-acre private park and its pleasant hosts at the neat old farmhouse in the clearing.

There is a natural bridge at Natural Bridge, New York, naturally, and it is on the map, right on N. Y. 3. It is a dozen miles northwest of Watertown, along the Indian River, and forms a tunnel that provides an underground boat ride of about 600 feet. It is owned and promoted by a garageman whose place of business is nearby. You have to duck, for it is "low bridge" in places, and not too remarkable or interesting. This natural bridge is, however, a true cave, in white limestone with another small cave under a hill nearby, in the midst of a level field. This can be traversed for 50 feet on hands and knees. It is dry and ends abruptly in a blank wall. It seems to be a remnant of a stream system that was left dry when the water found a lower level, through the natural bridge. This is in white marble adorned with a number of black, metallic-looking lumps that seem to be of magnetite ore—a strange and unusual combination, according to Mineralogist Anthony W. Thurston who investigated it.

Not far away is a very fine gorge, Whetstone Gulf, a narrow, twisting, 3-mile gorge ranging from 300 to 400 feet deep; and a convenient public camp site furnishes parking places for visitors. There is a cave in this area, near Lowville (N. Y. 12) known as the Hough Cave,[2] south of Martinsburg, on a side road to the west and about 3/4 of a mile from the entrance to Whetstone Gulf public camp site, and the entire area is a land of many lakes and streams and some reputed Indian shelter caves.

More interesting than the boat ride in Natural Stone Bridge, is the tall tale about its discovery, by one Alcasar Carr, who, while hunting, crossed Indian River on a log, walked on, circling, and to his astonishment, found himself back on the same side of the stream he had crossed.

He found that he had walked across the river on the stone bridge without knowing it at the time.

Then, also, there is the Bonaparte story, for Joseph Bonaparte, deposed king of Spain, bought a tract of land a mile square and built a house within 200 yards of the Stone Bridge, in 1829, and the owner of the Stone Bridge professes to believe that there was a secret passage from Bonaparte's house to the tunnel, emerging from the cellar, but for what purpose is a mystery, for Bonaparte was not in hiding by any means; indeed, he disported himself lavishly in public in this land of the free and haven of exiles.

There is also a natural stone bridge, a very small one, in the Catskills close to Old King's Road.

Joseph Bonaparte, who had an estate on a lake named for him, lying along the present N. Y. 3, about 30 miles east-northeast of Watertown, also has a cave named for him. Some reports have it more than one cave, but the only one that could be found and entered is little more than a porcupine den. It is near the shore of a little green-water pond not far from the uninhabited northeast side of Bonaparte Lake. Here is a patch of seemingly isolated limestone, sandy and soft. In it is a small hole which leads to a room large enough for a man to stand up in with bent head. The interior is a mass of fallen rocks through which passage can be made by crawling. It is not inviting, for the porcupines have left fertilizer strewn thickly on the floor.

The surrounding country is wild and entrancing, with sheer

[2]Hough's Cave, with its interesting history, is described in Chapter 14.

cliffs along the shore of Bonaparte Lake and more of them on an island. The cave is close to the Adirondack granitic rock formation. Solution of limestone is believed to have helped make the waters of the pond, called the Green Pond, their verdant color. There is no good land route to the cave; it is best reached by boat.

# *Chapter VI*

# CURIOUS CAVERNS

THE bottom fell out of a well in Pittsford one day, and the two daring lads who were digging it had the curiosity and nerve to go down and see what the bottom had fallen into. Ripley was not around at the time but you can believe it—or not—because none other than the town historian, who was also mayor and who is a chemist and metallurgist, tells the story—and he literally lives with the cavern which the boys found at the bottom of their bottomless well.

The cave was mentioned by Arch Merrill in his outdoor department conducted in the *Rochester Chronicle* and his book, *The Tow Path,* and as Mr. Frank W. Pugsley, Pittsford historian, describes it:

> The formation underneath our village is some thirty feet of shale known as Pittsford shale; underneath the shale is a formation of seventy or more feet of dolomite which is well honeycombed with crevices and caverns with quantities of water flowing through.
>
> The cave mentioned by Arch Merrill passes through underneath our village in a north and south direction, and nearly underneath my house. It was discovered by two young lads some fifty years ago while digging a well about ten rods from where I now live. They passed through the shale and were drilling and blasting in the dolomite. They had sunk about fifteen feet in this formation when they shot the bottom of the well out. Splicing on extra ladders they, with a lantern, descended and found a dry cavern, but water flowing nearby. After traveling in a northerly direction for some forty or fifty rods they retraced their steps back to the ladders and that was all the exploring ever done in this cavern. The hole was refilled and the cavern has remained a mystery ever since and very few people know anything about it now except some of the older residents like myself.
>
> Up to within a few years ago, before we installed a sewer system,

most of the sewage was disposed of by driving a pipe of about six inch diameter down to about thirty or forty feet in our back yard, to which the drain pipes from the house connected. The lower end of the pipe would usually connect with a cavern or crevice in the dolomite. By placing our ear to the pipe, water could be plainly heard rushing along below.

There are other reasons which have long led me to suspect that there may be some quite extensive caverns under this section.

It would seem that the roving Leatherman who got so many caves named after him in Connecticut, also wandered over into New York State, for J. Otis Swift in his "News Outside the Door" in the *New York World-Telegram* says:

> . . . near the Indian caves at Inwood Park, the Leatherman cave in Rock Lonesome and the cave where prehistoric men lived near Armonk in Westchester one comes upon rangy plants of poke, poke-weed, scoke, garget or inkberry, as our early settlers called it, because they squeezed crimson juice from the berries to make red writing fluid. . . . Does the inkberry still grow near old Indian caves and village sites because the squaws gathered it in autumn and used the berries to make colorful decorations and threw out the pulp and seeds to grow in their kitchen middens?

Mushrooms are grown in caves, cheese is cured in some; that is how you get domestic *bleu* cheese, comparable to the kind made in France and Italy, which is cured in caverns. Recently an enterprising man took over an abandoned limestone quarry which had been made a veritable cavern in the side of a hill in West Stockbridge, Massachusetts, and grows tons of the delicate edibles therein, and there are similar mushroom-growing plants in New York caves and old mines and quarries.

Mr. George Ward, of Clarksville, now retired, but who was a strawberry grower, has a curious cavern on his place, and one that once saved his strawberry crop from ruin by drouth, a loss he estimated would have cost him three thousand dollars. He piped water out of a deep underground lake in his cave and watered his berries all summer. The pipe still sticks down in the cavern from a hole in the roof, right over the lake.

Clarksville Cave or Caves, are close to the highway, New York 43, fifteen miles west of Albany. Old historical accounts describe two caverns, but recent explorers have failed to enter the second one, which has become closed. Its size, however, appears to have been exaggerated by the historians. The accessible cavern is a large one, in length, but not in width or height save at the inner end, where the lake lies.

This cavern is a tunnel through which flows the rippling waters of Oniskethau Creek. One account runs as follows:[1]

> The Clarksville Cave in its lower course is nearly filled with gravel and for a long distance is inaccessible. A short section may be entered near the road, running east and west through the village, and a short distance from the old hotel. It is called the "Little Cave." A longer section, the "Big Cave," is entered near the top of the hill north of the shorter part. The cave presents usually a smooth, rounded arch in the harder beds, though in the thinner beds the floor is littered with fragments and presents much of the appearance of a *Manlius* cavern.[2]
>
> A stream flows through it at all seasons and empties into the Onisthekau Creek south of the village. It is ponded in the larger section, some rods from the entrance and it would be necessary to build a boat in the cave to cross the water. It is quite possible that this stream enters the rock opposite the church, near Thompson's Lake, but this cannot be determined without further exploration. The cavern is in Onondaga limestone.

Further explorations have been made, several of them by experienced spelunkers, and at least one by a reporter and photographer from an Albany daily, their very first experience at spelunking, incidentally, and their account and their photos furnished a fresh series of views of this curious cavern.

This expedition was made on February 18, 1939, and we quote from the *Times-Union* account:

DE WITT TRIES HAND AT EXPLORING
CROSSES RIVER STYX—AT CLARKSVILLE

Party of 6, on Rubber Raft, Investigate Underground Lake
By DE WITT SCHUYLER

[1]Report of Geologist John H. Cook, 1906.
[2]Manlius limestone.

A home-town boy who has really made something of a name for himself in navigation circles is Captain Charon of the River Styx Night Line, who operates a bang-up ferry business on the principal stream of the lower world.

Even the legendary old salt himself, however, might have taken a few notes on the fine art of underground ferrying yesterday at the Clarksville Cave when an expedition headed by Roger Johnson, Springfield, Mass., pioneer cave-hunter and explorer of New England, made a successful crossing of the murky lake in the bowels of the earth that has defied cave-crawlers for several years.

ENTRANCE NARROW SLIT

Entrance of the cave, on the G. A. Ward farm in Clarksville, is a narrow slit in solid rock, barely wide enough to admit a man crawling on hands and knees. The peculiar rock formation, according to the owner of the farm, was the result of a dynamite blast set off in the cave by two men for some unknown reason about the turn of the century.

Thus it has been impossible to bring a boat down into the cave to explore the underground lake some 40 feet deep and 80 feet long which forms nearly three-quarters of a mile from the opening of the cave. A raft, crudely fashioned from logs once served as an explorer's aid, but it has long since rotted away.

SIX IN EXPEDITION

The Johnson underground-expedition, of which Clay Perry, Pittsfield author-sportsman; Arthur Palme, outdoor photographer, also of Pittsfield; Mr. Johnson's two sons, Stephen and Charles; George Burns, Times-Union photographer, and this reporter were members, made the passage with a ten-foot collapsible rubber boat which when blown up will carry two men in perfect safety. Among the other necessary gadgets taken along were strong ropes, shovels, crow-bars, powerful flashlights, compasses, hipboots, raincoats, cameras, maps, and other paraphernalia.

CAVERN WARM

Although ice and snow had formed a foot deep around the entrance and the wind was howling, it was nearly room temperature inside the cave. Drops of water oozed from rock formations as the party crawled on hands and knees along the labyrinth leading downward to a huge subterranean chamber. In the shifting glare of flashlights, the members were counted before the trek

NATURAL STONE BRIDGE AND CAVERNS, POTTERSVILLE, N. Y.

The forces of erosion in New York's Adirondack Mountains have carved out this natural bridge which is visited by hundreds of tourists each summer

Scene of many of the exploits of Deerslayer and Uncas, characters from the pen of James Fennimore Cooper, is this cave located at Glens Falls

The rocky gorge of Ausable Chasm is one of the scenic wonders of New York State's Adirondack Mountains. An exciting boat ride down the rushing waters of the Ausable River adds excitement to the scene. A "Devil's Hole" cave is one feature of the chasm

was begun along the slippery rock rising out of a running stream that sometimes reached above the knees.

The tortuous passageway dipped and bent through the earth, winding along jutting rocks and crevices for more than a half-mile when the first stop was made at the edge of the lake formed by the rushing underground streams. With Steve Johnson at the pump, the shapeless mass of rubber and canvas slowly billowed into a seaworthy craft, and was launched on the black waters ahead.

## CROSS UNDERGROUND LAKE

With Steve in the role of Charon, the party was ferried one by one across the deep channel over which the jagged ceiling hung scarcely three feet above. Then suddenly the channel emptied into a hollow rock basin, which held the underground lake, deep, treacherous, and black as any Styx. On the other side the expedition was set ashore amid the glistening rocks that formed its shore.

Once the return trip had been maneuvered, the boat was deflated and, equipment dangling from their shoulders, the cave-crawlers made their way back to the entrance.

*French's Gazeteer* of New York State, published in 1860, refers to the Clarksville Caves as follows:

> The entrance to the smaller cave, which is one eighth of a mile long, is from the rear garden of a village house. This cavern is connected with a larger one by a subterranean passage one half mile long. It is decorated with fine crystals of calcspar.

Unfortunately these crystals do not appear in the negotiable portions of the caverns today.

A later exploration, made by a combined New England and New York State party, occurred in the spring of 1946, and the stream was so low at the time that it was possible to traverse the entire half-mile tunnel without the use of a boat, but more easily with hip boots than without them, for those not thus equipped found it necessary to make several long and difficult belly-crawls along the ledges at the side of the stream, not to get wet to the knees. The temperature in this cavern was at that time 63 degrees Fahrenheit, due to the inrush of sun-warmed water, and the humidity was such that fog arose from the stream and bewildered the unfortunate wearers of spectacles, no end.

The dimensions of the cavern, as described above, are approximately true, the largest room, with its lake, being some 40 feet in diameter, plus the concealed portion which lies beneath a low roof which comes to within 2 feet or less of the surface of the lake. The roof is about 15 feet above the lake's surface at its highest point.

There is a legend about Clarksville Cave, or at any rate about the stream which flows through it.

The legend concerns "The Ghost of the Oniskethau," and tells of a mysterious trout fisherman who did his angling entirely at night and never failed to fill his creel from the waters of this creek. Local persons, out of curiosity, began to try to follow the lucky Izaak Walton, but he would disappear, and the story grew that he vanished into the cavern and caught his fish inside, in the dark, or by the use of a flashlight—but no one ever caught him at it.

Undoubtedly one of the strangest and most mysterious caverns in New York State is that which borders the shores of a little lake in the mountains of Austerlitz—or, rather, a combination of caverns, lake, mountain, and underground stream.

The place is named No Bottom Pond, and this name will be found on official maps of the region, together with nearby Fog Hill.

Here is a lake that disappears entirely, as if it were a mirage, and a hill that holds to its hollow perpetual fog! Well, almost perpetual. Persons who have visited this wild, remote place have never seen the hill or mountain hollow "without a hunk of fog in it thick enough to walk on," as a native guide described it once.

On the other hand, hunters and hikers who go to the No Bottom Pond, in spring or late fall, find it a placid little body of water surrounded by hardwood forest, and now and then someone has launched a boat on the lake.

But there is no need of a "No Fishing" sign here, for there are no fish in the lake; they just cannot survive because—in summer the lake is no longer there!

Just go and see for yourself!

This is not folklore or legend. I have walked, dry-shod, across this lake-bed. Friends of mine have gone boating upon the lake.

Here is how Richard F. Logan, geologist, spelunker, ex-chairman of the New England Spelunkers' Grotto, bicyclist whom I called "the human antelope" in a previous book, described his visit to No Bottom Pond and Caves, in the summer of 1937. (He did it on a bicycle, to a certain point.)

> Deep in the wild hills of Austerlitz a new cave has come to light!
>
> The scorching noonday sun on the Fourth found the geologist and his omnipresent bicycle, pedaling along the road atop the plateau north of that York State village in the vicinity of Fog Hill. Pausing long enough to wipe the perspiration out of my eyes, I took a look at the map and found that I was not far from "No Bottom Pond."
>
> A young man from Brooklyn paused in his job of polishing an auto long enough to answer queries. Yes, he knew about the pond —it was called that *because the water goes out of it at least once every year.* . . . No, it doesn't just dry up—*it runs out through one of the caves.* Yes, there are lots of them there—several in the bottom of the pond that you can go into when the pond is dry, and one at all times. . . . Yes, he would show me the trail and it is a fifteen-minute walk and there is a canoe on the pond.
>
> So, I set out merrily, afoot on that sunny July day, to visit the mysterious pond.
>
> And 'twas then that I first got the creeps. I've been startled before—as when a partridge flushes unexpectedly underfoot, or a rattler buzzes uncomfortably close; but I've never before had the creeps.
>
> First, it was the odor, as I approached the pond—sodden, damp, musty—as though dead things cluttered up the place. Then there was the quiet—not even a rustling of leaves on the trees or the chirp of a bird. And the toads made it worse. Thousands of them, newly hatched, hopped underfoot. The water was crawling with bloodsuckers and swimming with myriads of polliwogs and the "canoe" leaked frightfully and threatened constantly to dump me into the teeming water. I saw two snakes and the twisted stems of

grapevines looked like more.

The pond itself was disconcerting. In most places it was shallow, but in several spots it dropped off without warning into black depths.

I don't mind admitting that I thoroughly disliked the atmosphere of the place—that it got on my nerves and made me pretty jumpy.

I poked around in the dank woods till I found a spot where a fair-sized stream gurgled into a fair-sized hole in a ledge. It looked potentially crawlable.

It was with great relief that I emerged from the foul place into the sunlit upland pastures of Austerlitz. My car-polisher, half asleep on the grass, told me that I had not found *the* cave; the one I saw, he did not consider worth mentioning in his first directions.

So it looks like maybe the cavemen have more work to do. For I think I found a potential crawl for them—and I know I found a potential setting for a murder mystery.

Indeed, Dick Logan had found a setting for a *murder*—which had already happened before he was born.

It was near here that old Oscar Beckwith murdered his partner, Simon Vandercook, and tried to cook up Vandercook's body in a cookstove.[1]

With a guide who had lived in the town of Austerlitz in his youth and had hunted and fished around this area as an adult, I went to No Bottom Pond some years after Geologist Logan had visited it. There was a boat on the bottom of No Bottom Pond, but it could not be used because there was no pond. We walked across the semi-dry bed of the pond, followed the course of a trickle of water from a brook which calmly vanished in a hole about 6 inches in diameter in the bottom of No Bottom Pond. It was autumn; there were no toads or polliwogs to be seen. The rocky bottom of No Bottom Pond was slimy but there was no stench of dead things. There was fog in the hollow of Fog Hill, although the sun was shining on the other side of it.

[1]This story was told from the Massachusetts angle in the previous volume of "The American Cave Series," by Clay Perry, titled *New England's Buried Treasure*, the chapter headed, "The Gory Gold Mine Murder."

We found caves, a pair of them, opening in a limestone ledge on the shore of the vanished pond. One of them was large enough for a man to get down in a dozen feet or so, no farther. No sound of water issued from it; it was a dry cave. There were what the police call "suspicious" traces of some animals that had been here, perhaps bobcats, even some grayish hair caught on a splinter of a tree limb in the cave. No bobcat there, however. My friend said that the water that was running in that little hole—that "cave" in the bottom of No Bottom Pond—was believed to come out of the earth again some miles to the east, near State Line village. We did not even try to course down that stream, and it would take a very small amphibian troglodyte to do it. We did stop and look at a stream of water that issued out of a hole in the rock near the highway, about one mile as the crow flies or the water runs, from where it ran into the bottom of No Bottom Pond, but we cannot *prove* that this is the same water that leaks out of No Bottom Pond. We can prove that the water vanishes from that lofty pond which the Geodetic Survey maps tell us is at an altitude of 1,700 feet above sea level, while the outpouring water in State Line is at about 1,200 feet.

Another venturesome outdoorsman, a skilled hunter, Stephen "Turk" Miller of Pittsfield, Massachusetts, has seen No Bottom Pond both full and empty, has paddled about in a leaky craft on the water and trod in shoepacs across its dry bottom, and doubtless others have had similar experiences. It may be that old Oscar Beckwith, the murderer, took a shortcut across this pond or its bed in mid-winter in his flight from the scene of his ghastly crime. . . .

## Chapter VII

# ATROCITY IN AUSTERLITZ

BUTCHERED AND MURDERED

A HORRID MURDER
IN AN AUSTERLITZ MINING CABIN
THE VICTIM CHOPPED TO FRAGMENTS
AND BURNED IN THE MURDERER'S COOK STOVE!
AUSTERLITZ GOLD MINE AT BOTTOM OF TROUBLE

RUFFIAN AT LARGE

A REWARD OF $500 OFFERED FOR HIS ARREST.

These headlines in the *Chatham Courier* were echoed by numerous other newspapers in January, 1882, and for six years items appeared about the murder of Simon Vandercook by old Oscar Beckwith, his partner in an alleged gold mine somewhere in the wilds of the Austerlitz mountains, said to be on Varney Mountain, which at that time did not have such a name but was later named after J. M. Varney, who wrote a story of *The Life and Career of Oscar F. Beckwith, from the Cradle to the Grave.*

Beckwith believed that there was gold "in them thar hills," and got others to believe it, too. Especially Simon Vandercook, a woodchopper and farmhand, who had been an iron miner, and who became the partner and financial backer of Beckwith.

The gory tale is told in the preceding volume of this series, *New England's Buried Treasure,* from the Massachusetts angle, because it involved persons in the towns of Alford, North Egremont, Great Barrington, and Pittsfield, Massachusetts, and because Beckwith was a native of Alford, not of Austerlitz, as one recently published account has it.[1]

Mr. Walker evidently got much of his information from Varney, the old criminal's whilom biographer, who interviewed

[1] "The Beckwith Murder Case," by Warren Walker in *New York Folklore,* May, 1946.

him at the Hudson jail when the murderer was confined there. Beckwith was permitted the strange liberty of selling his memoirs at his cell door for a nickel or a quarter—and telling many lies.[2]

Mr. Walker's account is told from the standpoint of the Columbia County authorities, and no mention is made of the fact that it took a Massachusetts deputy sheriff to solve the case. It was Deputy Sheriff Humphreys of Great Barrington who trailed Beckwith; it was an Alford, Massachusetts, man who discovered the murder, an Alford posse that first attempted to arrest him; and none of them ever got the rewards that were offered by Columbia County, New York State, and Hudson.

But it all makes a bloody story and it furnished big black headlines for the newspapers, far and near, over a period of years.

Even the local merchants made capital of the case.

Two advertisements were run for weeks in the *Chatham Courier,* for instance:

UNCLE OSCAR BECKWITH
*The Austerlitz Cannibal would not be*
*in such a peck of trouble, if—instead*
*of nursing his morbid appetite—he had*
*taken a few treatments at*
PROF. E. W. HOWES'
*Electro-Therapeutic Institute*
*On Hudson Ave., Chatham, N. Y.*
*which would have placed him in a*
*condition to enjoy a common bill of fare.*
*Come and see the doctor whatever your*
*trouble. Consultations Free. Ladies under care of*
MRS. DR. HOWES'
*Galvanic Full Bath $1.00*
*Magnetic Sponge Bath .75¢*
*Local Treatment .50¢*
*Plain Water Bath .75¢*

---

[2]Mr. Walker's account was also drawn from the files of the Chatham Courier and other newspapers. We are indebted to him for permission to use parts of his article.

BECKWITH!
*The Austerlitz Murderer is to*
*be Executed on the 8th. of January, 1886.*
*And from now until that time we*
*are prepared to execute any orders*
*that may be left at*
HAMM'S
FURNITURE WAREROOMS

Curiously, toward the end, there arose much public sympathy for Beckwith, whose protestations of innocence changed, finally, to a highly colored story that he told of a fight for his life with Vandercook. Until the day before that set for his execution Beckwith expected a reprieve or commutation of his sentence by the governor, but he finally gave up and wrote his last letter, addressed to a daughter, a sort of will, leaving her some thirty dollars he had collected.

Records show that his execution on the gallows was "attended only by officials, clergymen and a company of infantry," but legend has it that the rope was too long and his feet dragged on the ground. He was "sprung" from the type of gallows then in use—and not "hung from a tree that is still standing," as was for years pointed out to the curious.

The account given by Harrison Calkins, the farmer who discovered the crime, points to Beckwith making his flight to Canada through New York State. Calkins, an expert horse trainer and driver, led a posse over a trail made by Beckwith's old horse, to a steep cliff on the New York State side of the border, in the direction of No Bottom Pond.

Since Beckwith believed or professed to believe that his shanty was in Massachusetts, he would hardly have doubled back into the Bay State and fled up through Vermont and New Hampshire, as the Varney account has it, for he would fear to run right into Calkins—who was a juryman, just excused from duty at Superior Court in Pittsfield. Beckwith knew that Calkins suspected him, as the old man was burning the hacked-up body of Vandercook when Calkins called at his door. Beckwith just lied to Mr. Varney.

STONE CHURCH CAVERN
An impressive and historic "open" cave at Dover Plains, N. Y., as seen in early spring

Entering the Amber Grotto in Adirondack Natural Stone Bridge and Caverns, Pottersville, in a rubber boat

Chimney Mountain and its great cleft caves in the last stand of Grenville limestone in the Adirondacks

One kind of cave equipment in use on an underground stream in New York State's limestone country

## *Chapter VIII*

# SOME SHAWANGUNK HIDEOUTS

Pompey's Cave, located in the village of Kyserike, which is within the township of Rochester, at the northern extremity of the Shawangunk Mountains, west side, near Mohonk Lake, was discovered by a Negro farm hand, in the 1850's. It served the dramatic purpose, later, of sheltering a woman and child and this escaped slave from raiding Confederates in the Civil War.

The story is little known and, in fact, never has been published, but it has been preserved in a manuscript that was written by Miss Margaret Atkins, while a student at New York State College for Teachers, in Albany. Professor Louis C. Jones, her instructor and editor of *New York Folklore,* handed the manuscript to me on my first visit to him. Miss Atkins became a school teacher in Schenectady, and a good one, and indications of her success as a pedagog are obvious in her student essay.

Miss Atkins got the story of Pompey's Cave from her grandfather, Henry Neff, who owned the estate on which the cavern is located and who was the first to examine the history and scientific features of the cave.

John Green beamed as he gazed at his wife, knitting in the peaceful light of the fireplace. "Her graceful movements are symbolic of our future life," he thought. "Easy, comfortable and carefree." Pompey, the Negro farm hand whom he had hired that very morning would do the work and keep this, his farm, in shipshape condition and he (Green) could spend the remainder of his life in rest and quietude.

This was in 1848 and Green's life continued as he had planned. His huge farm flourished under Pompey's hand. Though Pompey was working very hard, he enjoyed life, immensely, and extended his work into the further end of the estate that had not thus far been cultivated. Green didn't know what lay beyond the north pasture, himself.

One day as Pompey was taking the cows to pasture, they stopped to drink at the brook that ran through the field. The sound of a turbulent rush of water came to Pompey's ears. He was terribly frightened for he never had wandered this far on the vast estate before nor had he, on the other hand, seen anything particularly odd about the behavior of the brook, nearer the house, even though he had visited it every day. But as he stood there, waiting for the cows to finish drinking, he pondered on the strangeness of the noise. His fright was overcome by his curiosity and he ventured further along the bank. About six feet in front of him he saw the brook disappear with a thunderous splashing into a huge pit in the rocks composing the bank.

Pompey was not satisfied that the brook ended there. "It couldn't," he decided, and intelligently enough, "just go nowhere."

Pompey decided that this must have been meant to be his own, personal secret, and accordingly he told Green nothing of the incident.

Sunday morning found Pompey exploring that part of the farm which lay beyond the pasture lands. He found that the brook's disappearance was the cause of the excessive moisture in the cave and on the rocks that lay before him. A rock floor containing a cave with two mouths and one exit presented itself in the very center of the extreme end of the grazing fields. Where the brook seemed to drop into infinity, the level ground and the banks met with an extensive rock floor and steep rock ledges. On these ledges there were many peculiar lizards, snakes and curious plants that today constitute a great deal of the legend and beauty of the spot. A great snake seemed to be guarding the entrance to the cave. The mammoth reptile is named Big Pompey because of his seeming protection of the cave. This legend lives on. The trees and grass on the ledge provide homes for the numerous grass and tree snakes and various lizard types. A lynx, a very rare animal, is supposed to have some fantastic connection with the weirdness of the cave.

Scenically, the cave proper is unsurpassable, often providing advertising material for Kyserike. The picnic spot just above it resembles a well-furnished room. Along one side is a row of aged spruce trees. The section under them is carpeted by a soft covering of beautiful green moss. At the end of the "room," just above the cave, is a natural fireplace worn out of solid rock by flood waters. The area surrounding the mouth of the cave is as beautiful as the cave itself.

For many years after the discovery of the cave it was not penetrated nor was it carefully explored. It was not until 1919 that the proprietor realized that it could be a profitable landmark. Accordingly, he turned his home into a summer resort and prepared the cave for scouting and sightseers. A ladder was placed in the entrance and lanterns were provided to light the interior. Visitors enjoyed the short, interesting journey through the cave immensely.

Entrance is possible, to this day, through only one of the two mouths which are very close together. The stream flowing through the cave makes passage impossible in the annual spring flood season. In the bottom of the stream are many beautifully colored and curiously shaped pebbles. Their almost luminous qualities are fascinating and are quite parallel to those found in the Grand Canyon in Colorado. The floor itself is the bed of the various fossils which serve as an introductory study in the paleontology, also to a certain extent in the geology of the region. The walls of the cave are covered with moss. From the cracks in the walls trickles a constant stream of water which forms icicles in the fall and late spring.

Henry Neff made an amateur study of the interior of the cave. His findings were, for the most part, confined to fossils, such as the gastropod shell, most easily recognized, however the least valuable because it has been found in so many different places in more perfect condition. . . .

If Pompey's Cave were explored and annotated by a professional paleontologist, I believe it would prove to house many interesting geological details about the age of that section of Ulster County.

This cave has been explored by Roger Johnson, who reports that one needs rubber boots to get about in it with any comfort, but that it is exceedingly interesting for its natural features, and he also found it accessible for his mother, Mrs. Clifton Johnson, so evidently it isn't too tough for the fair sex.

You have to use candles for light in the Caves of Lake Mohonk. With characteristic conservativeness, the Smileys of the Lake Mohonk Mountain House bar the use of electric flashlights in their series of holes in the rock, to which guides take guests for a Sunday afternoon crawl.

You are not permitted to play golf or shoot craps on Sundays at Lake Mohonk, but you can keep the Sabbath "holey" if you wish by creeping into the Giant's Inn, or Ice Caves, or "The Place Where Humpty Dumpty Struck" when he fell, and, in place of skiing, slip and slither about through the snow, paved with ice, and get into quite warm, comfortable rock shelters. And then you may find ice on the floor and need ropes.

These are not limestone caves, but "accidental" ones, formed in the conglomerate rock of the region, making narrow, tortuous passages, twisting and turning at disconcerting angles, but with here and there a sizeable room and pebbled floors and crevices glittering with tiny quartz crystals.

From the "House," which has been famous for many years as a unique resort, established by the Quaker Smiley twins to replace a run-down roisterous beer-garden type of place that existed beside the lovely upland lake, it has become a custom to go caving every Sunday, in mid-summer. Starting out at about 3 o'clock in the afternoon in rough clothes, parties of from five to thirty, with guides, head for some known—or unknown—rock rooms in the wild country of the Shawangunk (Shongum is its pronunciation) Mountains.

> The management explains in an elaborate brochure written up for "The Mohonk Cavers," by A. Keith Smiley, Jr., "Since it has been the tradition to refrain from indulging in the ordinary sports on Sunday, it seemed fitting and natural that walks to the rocky areas and cave exploration should become the major pastime on Sunday afternoons. . . . On week-days it is only rarely considered as a proper pastime, while on Sunday, the thought of 'watching the cavers leave' or 'going caving' comes automatically to the minds of many who have summered frequently at Mohonk. . . .
>
> "Since the caves are unlighted and frequently narrow and winding, it is required that each caver be equipped with his own source of illumination. Flashlights, though sometimes used, are frowned upon by those who are well versed in Mohonk's caving tradition. Hence it followed that many a familiar passage is well marked by hardened drops of candle wax. In spite of hot wax

dropping on soft hands, singed hair and disconcerting draughts, tallow candles are universally employed for cave exploration at Mohonk. Besides adding a sporting element to the activity itself, pants well smeared with candle grease add an appearance of distinction to the attire of the seasoned caver."

It might be that the Smileys have also a cunning effect in mind, that is, to make the caves seem larger, darker, and more mysterious when seen only by the flickering flame of tallow tapers; and perhaps it would add even more thrills if birchbark torches or blazing pine knots were used, as it is believed that is how the Indians equipped themselves when they visited some of the Shawangunk caves, for:

The valleys were peopled by Indians, Iroquois, Algonquins and other tribes, fighting frequently and frequently moving, and all of them doubtless, when hard pressed, retreating to the labyrinths of the Shawangunk Mountains. There could be no more baffling maze for the pursuing enemy than what existed then and exists now in these mountains; and Mr. Smiley has frequently expressed the opinion that he could still hide in the vicinity of the lake so that he could not be found by anybody[1]."

In the vicinity of the Trapps are vast crevasses in the rocky ledges, some of them of unknown depth. These fissures vary in width from a few inches to as many feet, and constitute a feature of the natural scenery of the region.[2]

As to the caves that have been explored and named, the list suggests somewhat of a maze, indeed. There are caves in the Crevice, an open crack at the end of Sky Top Point, two of them, both vertical cracks from the cliff. Another, with "numerous caves," centers about "The Stovics," a series of passages in dislocated blocks of rock south of Eagle Cliff, a ridge west of Mohonk Lake, but even these caves, visited for years, gave up a "lost" one, which was named Cruikshank's Cave in honor of an enthusiastic spelunker.

"The Place Where Humpty Dumpty Struck" when he fell

[1]From *Legends of the Shawangunk,* by Philip H. Smith.

[2]From *The Story of Mohonk,* by Frederick E. Partington. Other references are many in Lake Mohonk's *Weekly Bulletin.*

off Eagle Cliff, is littered with holes, some large inside, one named Paul's Hole, a pit, deep and wide.

The Giant's Workshop area has the finest collection of caves, such as Newlin's, not far from Cope's Lookout and the Pole Cave or Giant's Inn, which has a legend about it. Here the Giant of the Shawangunks entertained his guests by running elevators, not up and down, but on the horizontal plane, in a loop. At one entrance is a steep descent into the Giant's Spring, one of the few Mohonk Caves that have water in them permanently.

Ice Caves are found in two localities, one some distance northwest of Bonticou Point, another along the mountain opposite Ellenville, deep rifts where snow accumulates and turns to ice, which is there most of the summer.

Schoolboys from the Mohonk School had a spurt of spelunking for some years, between 1921 and 1925, and found several new caves, extending the number of cavelets to be entered in the Humpty Dumpty and Giant's Inn areas.

The cave areas of the Shawangunk are very fine places to study the intricate geology of these mountains. The upper layer of rock is of hard quartz conglomerate, beneath which is shale; to the west both the shale and the conglomerate dip below the horizontal strata of sandstone and limestone that form the Catskills, so that as a rule the gentler slopes are on the west side of the range and on the east are sheer escarpments and cliffs revealing almost the whole thickness of the age of the conglomerate layer. Shale eroded rapidly, and left openings at the foot of the harder rock cliffs and even at the edges of the escarpment, likewise tumbling a talus which formed accidental cavities that make up most of the smaller caves.

The work of the last great glacier and of the subsequent thawing and floods of water are credited with forming these caves. They are interesting for their unexpected underground scenery, although they have no travertine formations.

Over to the north, in Kingston, are some caverns that are the results of mining for lime. They are known as water-lime mines, although for some years many persons have thought them to be natural caverns and at least one has been known as Cold Air Cave. Dr. A. Scott Warthin, Jr., of the geology department of Vassar College, who has made some study of this and other areas in Dutchess County, says there are several such mines beneath the city of Kingston, some of which have collapsed; others are full of water—and some were supplied with something stronger than water during Prohibition days. Stills were often located in the depths of these old mines and various kinds of hooch manufactured.

The caverns have caused not a little trouble in Kingston from time to time. One cave-in let a street down under, and it had to be filled with tons of rubbish, including wrecked automobiles, before the pavement could be restored.

One story of a sudden cave-in tells of a woman who lived on Hasbrouck Avenue, and who was walking about her lawn one day when the ground gave way beneath her and she was plunging into unknown depths. She managed to grasp hold of a rosebush and, despite thorn-scratched hands, pulled herself up and out. It is wise to walk softly in some sections of the city.

Another case of the ground giving away beneath a person's feet is cited by W. W. Mather in his *Geology of New York*.

A farmer, Mr. Cronkite, who lived near Round Pond, four miles southwest of West Point, Orange County, was digging a pit to bury potatoes for the winter, when rocky land gave way and exposed a cavern extending 30 or 40 feet from the pitfall. Mather explored it in 1825 "in various directions" and reported the roof to be studded with minute, brilliant crystals of various materials, such as hexagonal crystals of mica, hornblende, spinelle, augite, etc. The cavern is now filled up by wash of earth and deposit of stones to keep cattle from falling in.

Another example occurred near Pine Plains on the line of a sunken stream. A cow fell into the cavern and died for want of food and water, although there was plenty of the latter beneath her. The trees were not disturbed by the cave-in, curiously.

Caverns of any considerable size or with dripstone deposits are rare in Dutchess County, which Dr. Warthin attributes to the fact that the only widespread limestone, the Wappinger, is so folded and fractured that it does not lend itself well to cave development, and most of the caves are very small, not more than 3 by 4 by 20 feet. In a purer streak of limestone near the hamlet of Eighmyville, east of Rhinebeck, is a good but small cave, reputed to be over 100 feet long, with some dripstone deposits, as reported by G. B. Shattuck in *Geological Rambles near Vassar College*.

Doubtless the most interesting things about the caves or old mines and quarries in the vicinity of Kingston, Binnewater, Rosendale, and Rondout are the fossilized rocks which have been turned up by the bushels in quarrying and mining operations.

Limestones of many different sorts cropped out around these places and as early as 1818 a French engineer, named Vigat, discovered "natural cement rocks" in a belt extending southwestward from Kingston to the northeastern end of the Shawangunks. This led to extensive developments that are still in process, the quarrying, milling, and shipping of this material, much of which went into the building of Brooklyn Bridge, at the height of the era.

Mohonk Caves are a premier attraction at Mohonk Lake Mountain House area

Alcove of the Angels,
Howe Caverns

# Chapter IX

# SINKS OF SCHOHARIE

A SINKHOLE or rockhole in limestone country, especially if there is running water near, is a good indication that there may be caves in the area. Schoharie County is full of sinkholes and rockholes and underground drainage systems, and plenty of good caves. There are more than twenty known, named caves in the county, most of them quite thoroughly explored, some developed as tourist attractions.

According to published accounts, some of the caverns have been known since the 1830's, perhaps even earlier, as one or two have reputations as being Tory hideouts in Revolutionary times and one or two as refuges for earlier settlers against Indian attacks, or as being used by the Indians themselves as shelters or retreats from their tribal enemies.

The town of Schoharie, the county seat, gets some of its water supply from streams flowing underground, and students of the geology of the area believe that this portion of the water for the town is furnished by Ball's Cave, one of the most interesting, largest, and most described undeveloped caverns in Schoharie County. It was first thoroughly explored in the 1830's, and noted in the history of the county shortly after.

Once known as Gebhard's Cave, it is difficult to find and must be located by following careful directions or with a guide. The opening is a vertical shaft in Coeyman's limestone, on the north side of Barton Hill, three-fifths of a mile southwest of the point where the road to Quaker Street crosses the county line.

It can be reached conveniently only by an old farm road that starts from the house known once as the Edwin Dietz home, now the Wilbur farmhouse. On the way across the meadows, in a swale, there is a sinkhole, which leads nowhere, but which serves as a marker and a sign of cave country.

The oldest known official account of this cave was written from personal observation of it by Jeptha R. Simms in his *History of Schoharie County,* published in 1845. It reveals that John Gebhard, Jr., one of the early students of geology and mineralogy of the region, was largely responsible for the discovery and also the rape of the cavern of many of its formations, which he did in the name of science and to add wonders to his collection of minerals and formations, at one time famous.

Ball's Cave, says the historian, known as Gebhard Cave, after John Gebhard, Jr., who owned it in 1842, is on Barton Hill, in a dense patch of woods.

"It was first partially explored in September, 1831, and on October 21st of the same year, Dr. John Foster, Mr. John S. Bonny, John Gebhard and others of Schoharie, having prepared a boat, again visited this cavern, and being let down with ropes, with their skiff, they pretty thoroughly explored it."

They named their skiff the "Bonny Boat," and it must have been a very small one, indeed, to get it down the narrow shaft and drag it through a low archway scarcely large enough to admit a man, to get it to the most constantly watery part of this cavern.

"It (the chimney-like entrance) was then partly covered with tree trunks (and) was 70 feet deep and 12 feet across."

In four pages of description Simms reveals that the cavern was literally plastered with beautiful formations, and that the explorers pretty well stripped it of them, even to one slab or hunk of "alabaster" weighing several hundred pounds that was hauled to the bottom of the perpendicular shaft by main strength, then hoisted with a windlass, "to be added to Mr. Gebhard's cabinet."

Others who followed completed the wreckage of almost every one of the beautiful stalactitic and flowstone formations.

These explorers left their mark in other ways. They named one room the Music Saloon, because of the echoes it afforded to voices and the trickle or burble of running water. Another they called Passage of the Dams, and another The Fox Room.

Simms describes what he calls a lake as being 400 feet in length and 8 or 10 feet wide, with an average depth of 6 to 30 feet, and he or the explorers seem to have first named the Rotunda Room, and measured it as 315 feet in circumference. There were some 30 persons, equipped with torches, in the cave when Simms visited it, and the walls and ceiling were littered with hibernating bats.

"Tons of rare minerals were removed, including stalactites, stalagmites of semi-transparent alabaster, white as Alpine snow, slabs of alabaster, satin spar, crystals, etc."

The huge slab that Gebhard took out was pulled out of the Music Saloon, where also was found a female bust or breast of purest alabaster and "the contour is French," says the observant historian, and *"approximates surprisingly to nature,* on which account it is one of the most valuable of all stalagmitic formations, for it is a form which may be admired without fear of its imbibing *false pride,* or blushing at the exposure of its own charming proportions."

One wonders what ever became of this female form divine.

Females explored this cavern, among them one, Miss Wyland, "a spirited and intelligent young lady from New York City" who appears to have been the original of a "romance of the Mohawk," by Hoffman, titled, *Greycelear,* which has some of its scenes located in the cavern, which he named *Wenonda.*

The fictional heroine was named Alida de Rose, but Historian Simms opines that the character was perhaps based on Miss Wyland, "who must have been very beautiful."

One adventure that was experienced by Mr. Bonny in his "Bonny Boat" was nearly tragic, or at least might have been. He was pulling his skiff over one of the fourteen tufa dams in the Passage of the Dams when he nearly lost his balance and fell in, and would have "lost his light and had to swim a quarter of a mile in total darkness in icy water to get out," observes Simms. But it didn't happen. He lived to roam other caves with Gebhard, including Nehtaway's Cave on the Peter Nethaway farm, 2 miles southwest of the Court House at Schoharie, and "nothing worth removing save some spar" was found, which "looked like maple sugar."

The vertical shaft of Ball's Cave, today, is only about 40 feet deep, because of the deposit of debris through the years, but, being perfectly perpendicular, is deep enough, especially as an ancient ladder made of tree trunks with cross-pieces spiked on them is rather treacherous and bears out the warning sign "At Your Own Risk," on a nearby tree, especially in winter when the rungs are coated with ice inches thick.

This is how our Yankee spelunkers found it on my first visit, after plowing through wet snow for over a mile.

The cavern has been dissolved out of the basal Manlius beds, and at some seasons the whole cave is filled with water; at others, parts of it are totally dry, even the stream bed where we had to wade to our knees in rubber boots and later paddled about in a rubber boat upon it.

From the bottom of the well-like entrance, a sloping passage with rough, loose rocks on its slippery floor, leads down to a sharp left turn. Just before this turn is an opening, at the right, such a low stone arch as we find in Lizard Cave in Catskill, and this becomes completely blocked up by the wash of water, time after time. Our first visit found it so, and we considered it impassable. It was, for lack of tools to dig with. A second visit, in summer, found this archway dug out and crawlable—into the most interesting part of the cavern, to my eyes.

Here is an underground acqueduct or canal, immediately suggestive of the subterranean drains or waterways that are to be found in some of the cities of the British Isles and Europe. The water is clear as crystal and icy cold. It has formed a series of tufa dams, from deposits of limestone that looks as if they had been made by human hands. Some of our party insisted that they had been man-made for they were so perfect in construction, with small sluice-ways cut into them through which the water dribbled in small streams. In places behind these several dams the water is 7 feet deep. From the overflow at the first dam to which one comes, this arched, rounded tunnel extends for 330 feet into a chamber at a higher level, beyond which the passage is so small and so filled with water and soft, clayey mud, that it is dangerous if not entirely impassable, save with a diving suit.

This expedition was one part of a national speleological trip, which brought delegates of the National Speleological Society from far and near, including President William J. Stephenson, of Washington, D. C., and J. S. Petrie, Secretary, from the same city, a carload from Cleveland, Ohio, and a dozen persons from New England. All save one or two with a bit of claustrophobia went into Ball's Cave. A quartet of us, equipped with rubber boots, warm clothing, gloves, crept into the tufa dam chamber and to our delight discovered that someone had managed to construct a raft out of some boards wired to a large automobile inner tube that was still holding air.

Straddling this raft, I started off on a Charon voyage and within a minute had slipped in, over my boots, and swiftly retreated and left the tipsy raft to float down. Petrie then tried it, and the tricky thing dumped him in the 7-foot pool and he came up totally soaked. No more voyaging on that raft was tried, but one of the party succeeded in wading along the edges and on the tops of the tufa dams to a point 50 or 60 feet upstream, after which there was no thoroughfare save for fish. The odd perfection of those tufa dams and the bluish, clear water makes this chamber charming beyond description and of great interest to the scientist spelunker, as well.

Taking the left turn, outside, one gets right into the exposed stream or the bed of the stream, wades or paddles or just walks for 200 feet to a mass of fallen fragments which are slippery with clay and furnish an obstacle of no mean sort, requiring a scrambling climb, some boosting and helping hands from above, to get up to the Rotunda Room, the hugest in the cavern.

Before ascending, there is a study in rifts and clefts which open at one side and opposite the bulwark, rising to awe-inspiring and unclimbable heights to the lofty roof, and "painted" with sparkling calcite minerals and drops of water. Bats hang all about here in winter.

The Rotunda Room has some remarkable features other than its immense size. It is approximately circular and from 40 to 50 feet each way, with a solid, slightly sloping ceiling of rock 12 feet above the highest point of a huge bank of clay-covered rock that slopes steeply to one wall, also of solid, unbroken rock. This bank, when wet, makes a marvelous underground ski hill. We booted spelunkers sat on our heels and took the slide with great glee, then climbed up into passages leading away from the Rotunda Room, one of them a roundabout journey of many rods, to a point where it circles back on itself and returns the explorer to near where he started.

There is a closed room in Ball's Cave where the skeleton of a fox was found many years ago, and it became closed when a spelunker, with an Indian for a guide, was in the cave, a rockfall occurring which just missed burying them alive. A map of Ball's Cave drawn by Professor Cook and published in his 1906 report, shows this Fox Room, a tiny grotto on the left side of the main passage just after the first left turn, below the vertical shaft. This map also shows but nine of the fourteen tufa dams in what is called the Square Room (the origin of the stream, apparently).[1]

In a study of Schoharie County geology, A. B. Grabau, State Paleontologist, at Albany, in 1906 reported on an extensive exploration of Ball's Cave. He said that it was first discovered by Peter Ball, the owner of the property, and then passed on to W. H. Knoepfel, who announced his intention of opening the cavern to the public in 1854. The project, however, was abandoned and, says Mr. Grabau, "the condition of the cavern is today what it was 75 years ago."

Alas, he did not know the half of it, for the Gebhard-Bonny rock-snatchers had, long before 1854, removed every bit of formation they could drag out, and others followed their ex-

[1]See end papers for corrected map of Ball's Cave.

ample, and in 1906 there were few left save in what was called the Fox Room, which later became closed.

Apparently the first formal report on Ball's Cave was made in *The American Journal of Science* in 1835, by Dr. Charles U. Shepard, of Yale University. A Mr. Hubbard and Mr. Branch, in company with Gebhard, measured the cavern in 1831, as described in the main text of this book, and their measurements reveal that since then a great deal of change has taken place within its recesses, shortening the entrance shaft, for instance, from 75 feet to about 40 feet, by the piling up of debris at the bottom.

Grabau describes the cavern from hearsay, to some extent, seeming never to have gone into it himself; if he did, he did not see all there was to be seen, but he did see things which cannot be seen today and heard an "Aeolian harp" being played by the wind in one of the small adits, of which he counted five, but "all small and none remarkable."

A group of spelunkers from Sidney, led by Donald L. Palmer, a member of the N. S. S., and well equipped, they supposed, for thorough exploration of the cavern, "found so much water in there that it was impossible to ride a boat on the surface, which was very close to the roof in many places."

This was on February 9, 1947, with snow deep on the ground, almost concealing the sinkhole entrance.

"In fact the water level was so high that one could barely lie horizontally between the top of the water and the ceiling. (And who wants to float in water at 47° F.?) We had to use the small boat to get to where we could get photos of the bats, whereas on a previous visit (November 9, 1946) we could walk everywhere but on the water. We could crawl into the lake room, which means that the water level was up some seven feet on February 9," reports Mr. Palmer.

These lads had two rubber life rafts, one for two men, the other for four, and a thirty-foot rope ladder and one hundred feet of five-eighths-inch rope, three kerosene lanterns, a four-cell floodlight, two-cell waterproof lights, two pairs of hip boots, matches, candles, twine, a tank of carbon dioxide to inflate the rafts, cameras, flash-bulbs, thermometer, etc.

They found but a single sizeable rockflow formation in the entire cavern, a pillow-shaped block in the Rotunda Room, amid a rubble of fallen stone.

The closed room where the rockfall occurred was walled, with natural masonry effect, by thin slabs of limestone. Cook named it the Broken Room.

There is a tempting lure about Ball's Cave; it might well be developed as a commercial cavern, of all that are to be found in Schoharie County, but it was passed up in the 1920's when an ambitious man started to develop another one, not far from it.

Just where the water runs from Ball's Cave is still unknown, but the chances are it runs from the faucets of the homes and stores of Schoharie town. The present, modernized supply comes from a series of springs at the foot of a hill to the northeast of Schoharie, across the Foxenkill, on the Gallupville Road. Mayor Badgley and Historian Arthur B. Gregg have often discussed the possibility of their source being the extensive stream flowing through Ball's Cave, which lies on top of this hill, directly back of the springs. This possibility is also indicated in a study by A. W. Grabau in his *Guide to the Geology and Paleontology of the Schoharie Valley in Eastern New York, 1903*.[2]

It is possible that a test may be made by the use of dye, which

[2]Arthur Van Voris, who explored Ball's Cave in 1928 found "a very large stalagmite of pure white formation," on the north side of the Rotunda Room, where the side wall meets the floor—but, alas, it was not there ten years later when I visited it. Van Voris said that it was a mass weighing perhaps 300 pounds, but had been considerably chiseled, its beauty marred, when he saw it.

He also saw a strange sort of plant growing near a crystal pool at the base of the "ski slide," a vine-like plant, brownish in color and rather woody and brittle to the touch, having grown without a single ray of sun or light save from the feeble flashlights brought in by explorers at rare intervals. Some small, growing stalactites were noted by this spelunker, and he discovered the name "J. B. Sellick" carved on the ceiling of one passage, a name which is given to another cave in Schoharie County, but spelled "Selleck," although it seems to be the name of the same man.

Watkins Glen, here seen from the bottom of its rocky gorge, is a scenic public park maintained by the state of New York. It has some pothole caves

Natural cross section of
a stalagmite,
Howe Caverns

has been used to some extent in the Thacher Park area and caves.

In addition to this modern interest, there is some evidence that the cave may have been used at one time as a Tory hideout. Historian Gregg, who has some relics of Peter Ball, who was chairman of the Schoharie Committee of Safety during the Revolution, says there were many Tories in the region and that Peter Ball knew them and their refuges and "there may be more truth than fiction in the (story of the) use of the cave on Ball's property as a Tory rendezvous."

Becker's Cave, under Laselle Park, in the town of Schoharie, was closed for a time, but was explored by Dr. Cook in his survey, the report of which was published in 1906. The entrance was at the bottom of a low cliff, behind the Lutheran cemetery. It opened in or near the base of the Manlius limestone.

Dr. Cook wrote:

> This clearly does not represent the mouth of a cavern. For 115 feet the passage is just high enough to enable one to creep, is between two and five feet wide and slopes noticeably downward. This part is nearly straight, the general direction being S.15 e (magnetic). It broadens gradually to ten feet toward the further end where the floor drops sufficiently to permit of standing erect. Here a drain has been developed in the west wall. This is fairly commodious for thirty-eight feet but drops abruptly to harder beds upon which the water has acted more slowly and the remainder of the passage extends due west for sixty-eight feet as a widened joint, can be traversed only by lying flat. At the further end a crevice in the floor too small to penetrate serves to carry off the water to still lower beds, probably to Rondout dolomite.
>
> The main passage was followed for 230 feet beyond the drain to where a small side passage enters from the north. Further exploration was prevented by ponded water and the low roof. This part of the cave is full of clay and one must progress on hands and knees for almost the entire distance. No stream was flowing through it at the time of this visit and the pools contained no life. Neither stalactites nor stalagmites were found.

The largest cavern in Schoharie County is, of course, Howe Caverns, one of two commercialized caves in the region, and the most beautiful in New York State. It has a romantic history as well. Secret Caverns, its companion tourist attraction, much smaller, is quite beautiful in its half-mile extent, presenting in miniature some formations similar to those at Howe, and boasting a waterfall. These will be treated elsewhere, for the "wild caves" of the county, very little known, present some rare bits of history and legend and are of considerable beauty.

A cave near Shutters' Corners has almost as many names as a much-divorced woman. It has been called Spadeholt's Cave, Nasholt's Cave, and Treddlemire's Cave, as well as Shutters' Corners Cave. It is on the Delos Treddlemire farm, just a bit off the Shutters' Corners road, 4 miles east of Schoharie on N. Y. 43, close to the first house east of a schoolhouse. In the late 1920's this cave was leased and efforts made to enlarge the entrance and some of its passages, to furnish a picturesque walk and a boat ride on a beautiful blue lake inside. After building plank walks and extending electric lines in waterproof cables far inside, the project failed, due to the depression of the 1930's, and the whole thing was abandoned. The walks and cables, light sockets, and a large engine set up on concrete outside, were left to rust and rot; and then nature, seeming to resent the blasting and digging that had been done at the entrance, let some tons of earth slide down over the opening, and closed it.

But it was not to remain closed to such an energetic and persistent spelunker as Roger Johnson, who drove up atop the hill which the cave penetrates from a deep gully, and, equipped with shovel, pick, and two young sons as helpers, dug the earth mass away until they could get inside. This was in 1939. He crawled in, stood up and walked for 500 feet, then crawled and walked 500 more to where the passage narrowed to a width of 2 feet. Below the passage a small, deep lake could be seen through crevices, a lake with but 3 feet of headroom from its surface, which would hardly have provided a comfortable boat ride.

The cave contains many formations, very beautiful stalactites and stalagmites, many of them broken off by the "development" work or by vandal visitors, and fragments litter the floor.

When the Johnson party came back to the entrance they found that there had been another earth slide while they were inside, but it was not serious. They dug themselves out, and returned, with others, for further exploration. Some rapid changes occur in some caves, and this and Ball's Cave are among those that have changed in a few years, due mostly to the rise and fall of water. Shutters' Corners Cave was shut off at about 200 feet, inside, when we visited it last.

A party of seven men, four of them members of the State Museum staff and one of them a minister who had visited it forty years earlier, explored this cavern in 1928. They had to dig their way in, under the direction of Reverend J. Judson Westfall. A report on this expedition was made by D. H. Newland of the Museum and published in *The Knickerbocker Press* of Albany, in August, 1928. The measurements made showed that the entrance was a shaft about 12 feet deep from which a 45-degree passage lead 15 feet, after which the level of the cave changed very little. They penetrated by winding passages for about 670 feet, and found uncertain evidences of what may have been another entrance, fragments of wooden ladders, for one thing, but could find no opening at the time. The passage beyond this point was blocked by debris but the Reverend Mr. Westfall remembered that, as a boy, he had gone farther than this.

No such distances were possible to negotiate in 1939 when Mr. Johnson and I visited it, and it is probable that great cave-ins have taken place there, perhaps caused partly by the excavating done when it was invaded to commercialize it, and partly by the rush of water.

Arthur Van Voris, who visited it shortly after the Museum party did, states that the water in the cavern was being used as a domestic supply for the nearby farm owner, who had placed a mechanical pump at a strategic spot to force water through pipes several hundred feet.

Clark's Cave or Shelter Cave is a small opening in a cliff behind a house known as Samuel Clark's place on the north side of Schoharie Creek and not far from the town center. It was excavated from the basal beds of Becraft limestone, and is dry save in spring, and after exceptionally heavy rains at other times. It can be crept into for not more than 30 feet and is not remarkable in any way.

Van Vliet's Cave opens in the lower Rondout beds in a field about a mile north of the Gebhard Bridge, which crosses Schoharie Creek in the town.

It is crawlable not more than 100 feet with any degree of comfort, and is remarkable only for the presence of a few fossils in the slabs of limestone. Fossils, incidentally, are scattered about in great numbers in the Schoharie area. Mr. Richard Van Vliet, for whose family this cave was named, and who lives at the end of the Gebhard Bridge, on the downstream side, has the hugest single, private collection of fossils in New York State. He has filled to the roof a sizeable cottage on his place, with fossils to astronomical numbers. He has piled many more rock-bedded fossils around the cottage on the ground, some of them weighing many pounds. He estimated in 1939 that he had over 30,000 of them which he had picked up in roaming about the region, many of them in caves.

One can walk on fossils in some of the quarries and cut banks and stream beds of Schoharie County, all sorts of them, from the impressions of prehistoric ferns and stalks to marine creatures who left their signatures by the imprint of their shells in clay that hardened to rock. This makes good limestone.

In the little village of Carlisle Center, which is on U. S. 20, west of N. Y. 148, and not far from Central Bridge, is Selleck or Sellick Cave, a deep fissure traversing both Coeyman's and Manlius. It was visited by Dr. Cook in 1905 and described as being on the farm of Chester Othman, on the Cobleskill-Carlisle Road, one mile southwest of Carlisle Village, but he said that "the passage through which running water flows is blocked off from the fissures by the rubbish which has fallen through and almost closed the entrance."

But the very industrious explorer, Arthur Van Voris, visited it some twenty years later, and in his manuscript history of "Lesser Caverns of Schoharie County,"[3] which he made available to me, he remarks that he had been unable to turn up any detailed description of it prior to his expedition, which was a well-organized one.

There had been some confusion in the past concerning the location of Selleck Cave, as it had been sometimes referred to as McFail's Hole, but Van Voris decided that they are two separate caves, in the same general area. This is probably due to something that was discovered at the bottom of Selleck Cave, as will be seen, later.

The Van Voris party of seven strong men tied a rope to an overhanging limb of a tree that was conveniently right above the "chimney hole" in the dark woods. They descended 125 feet, straight down a narrow crevice, "and found themselves on a floor strewn with many specimens of translucent rhombohedral spar of gorgeous amber color, pieces of varied size that in times past had fallen from the high ceiling of this chamber. To the left was an archway hewn from solid rock by Nature, and by crawling on hands and knees under it, directing lights ahead, an underground lake was seen swinging off into a waterway with walls and ceilings as round and smooth as can be imagined."

From the description given by Van Voris, Selleck Cave seems to have been one of the very few unprotected caverns in this area which had not been almost completely robbed of their fine formations, perhaps because of the great difficulty of getting in and out of it.

Selleck Cave, he writes, "literally abounds in beautiful translucent side-wall formations," with "tons and tons of this amber-colored flowstone extending from floor to ceiling as far as a searchlight would carry. It was formed in strips and waves that

[3]Also deposited in State Museum.

looked much like strips of bacon, very beautiful to look at in the light of the searchlights that brought out the translucent effect.[4]

At a distance of about 400 feet from the bottom of the well-like shaft entrance, the party came to a narrowing down which stopped them, but their lights shone through a crevice for perhaps 30 feet. As they had come down a rope in the well, 100 feet or more, and then had scrambled down a steep slope for 30 feet more, and had hard going through the long passages, they did not attempt to squeeze through the crevice.

But after brushing past a pendant, balanced rock that could be moved on its base, they came upon an inscription which seems to be a simple epitaph to an early cave explorer.

Carved deeply on the side-wall formation, and perfectly legible despite some flowstone having dripped over it, was the inscription "T.N.M.–1844." Probably the initials of T. N. McFail.

Dr. Cook tells us that George Sibley and J. C. Sellick first visited this cave in the year 1841 and that they reported that "it afforded the visitors fine specimens of spar."

Here appears a cause for some of the confusion about Sellick Cave and McFail's Cave–for *Professor T. N. McFail lost his life in another, nearby cave while exploring it in 1853,* but evidently he had explored this one. The story of this tragedy is told in the *History of Schoharie County,* by William E. Roscoe, as follows:

> Professor McFail of Carlisle Seminary, an accomplished gentleman, met an untimely death at the entrance of the cavern after exploring its depths with others in 1853. The Professor was on a rope used to draw persons up from the pit and coming in contact with the outer air, he fainted and fell backward, striking upon his head which badly fractured the skull and from which he survived only a short time. Since that time, few if any visits have been made to the cave.

McFail was a geologist of some note and evidently had been investigating several of the caverns in the Carlisle area. There seems to have sprung up a spontaneous wave of exploring, for

[4]Such formations are rare, usually found only in large southern caves.

geological reasons, in the period from 1830 to 1850, in this region. It was during this era that many fine caves were found, such as Howe Caverns, which Historian Simms describes as Ostagaragee Cavern, and says that G. F. Yates was one of the first visitors to enter and describe it after Lester Howe had discovered it in 1842.

But to return to a further exploration of Selleck Cave. In 1928 some residents nearby determined to try to get across the underground lake they had seen on their first visit. They obtained a collapsible canvas boat, a sort of skiff, and lowered it by ropes to the cavern floor, down the rocky entrance and shoved it under the stone arch into the little lake. Two men got in, with lanterns and electric torches. At the point of embarkation the water was not more than 3 feet deep but ample to float a light canvas craft. They shoved along, carefully, some 30 feet, to a turn, finding that the water grew very deep, but was so clear they could see the bottom at an estimated depth of 25 feet. They got into a lofty chamber arching over the lake, and began to hear the sound of a waterfall which they had previously heard but could not see. From the boat they could look up the side wall and see a gushing stream pouring from a hole about 20 feet from the lake surface, cascading down merrily into the lake. Here also they saw "two natural stone columns looming high to the ceiling, with thin edges that crumbled at the touch and which gave forth musical sounds when blown upon by air currents."

There was also noted another water-filled passage entering the lake chamber, its extent visible for from 15 to 20 feet, but impassable, as the roof lowered to the water. They estimated they had voyaged about 150 feet from the archway, on this lake, and decided to turn back and join their two companions whom they had left at the archway.

Suddenly, in making a turn about a rough stone column, the canvas boat struck a jagged rock that tore a hole in it and flooded it. The unlucky voyagers were sunk, their lantern and one of their torches vanishing and leaving them in total darkness for a moment. One electric flashlight, however, was clung to, and by its light the young, vigorous farm lads swam back to the archway in the chilly water.

McFail's Hole, located in the midst of a deep wood on the Ira Young farm near Carlisle Center, is somewhat similar to Selleck Cave, and has a companion opening near it that adds to the confusion, and which is remarkable for its coldness, for even on a hot summer afternoon icy air comes forth so that one can see one's breath at the rocky entrance, despite which it appears to be the haunt of many bats.

The true McFail Cave is approached by a characteristic sink-hole, at the bottom of which is a convenient rock platform from which one may look down many feet of sheer rock, an extension of this ledge; on the other side the shaft cuts off about 15 feet from the floor, evidencing an entrance to some inner chamber. Logs had been thrust into this shaft, it is believed, after Professor McFail lost his life here, and they hindered descent but did not prevent it, ropes being used for the plunge down to the first level. Determined explorers managed to clear away some rubbish of rocks and wood in an effort to find an outlet from this chamber—and suddenly, as they worked, a whole corner of the chamber caved in and the debris vanished with a great booming and thunder into a perpendicular well!

To find out how deep it was, a lantern was lowered and the well discovered to be 44 feet deep, leading into an elliptical room with fine opaque travertine on one wall, in the shape of a triangle, practically the only formation of note in the cave.

This appears to be the same cave which Dr. Cook called Wolfert's, because when he explored it Alonzo Wolfert owned the property. Cook described it as a few rods east of the highway, one-third mile due north of Howe Cave Village.

Professor Cook had men with him to help, and long ropes, a lantern, and a lot of courage and determination. The entrance was made by way of a nearly horizontal tunnel, with a trickle of water running into it, a crawlway of a few yards—and then the caveman came to a sudden drop-off. Cook had himself lowered into a circular hole or well, by a rope, until he could stand on a shelf, 45 feet down. Here he lowered his lantern with a cord, until he could see that there was some bottom to the well. Near the bottom, also, was another shelf, 45 feet further down, a total distance of 90 feet or more, and in the very bottom of this cylindrical hole were numerous smoothed rocks of various sizes, many of them as perfectly round as marbles.

Seeking the cause of this phenomenon, Professor Cook found a tiny drain hole on one side of the shaft, too small for him even to put his foot in, and he had the answer to this stone smoothing. Water had at times rushed into the well from above so rapidly that it formed a whirlpool at the bottom and rolled the rocks around and around. They could not get out the drain, and what with grains of sand to help in the rounding process, the deep well had been a natural stone mill.

Professor Cook had previously visited the Barytes Mine, mentioned in Hovey's *Celebrated Caverns,* and he believes that the water from Wolfert's Cave made its way under the hill into this lengthy cavern, now filled in with clay, but at that time connected with Howe Caverns.

Jack Patrick is a name to conjure with, and a cave was conjured on his old farm, near the head of a gorge that opens into the Cobleskill Valley, on the back road between Howe Cave Village and Central Bridge. It parallels Howe Caverns and "may reach beyond Grosvenor's Corners where a small underground stream is to be found," entering another descriptively named hole in the rock, Pigmy Cave, as Professor Cook calls it. This is on the old William Passage place, between Grosvenor's Corners and Carlisle Center. It is very small, as may be gathered, but leads to Young's Cave, in Cook's lexicon of cavities, which got its name from Spencer Young, on whose farm it was discovered, one-half mile due west of Carlisle Center. It is in Becraft limestone. This cave, in turn, discharges its stream into the southern end of the trough at the opposite extremity of which is McFail's Disappointment Cave. The roof has fallen in for most of its length, but about 250 feet of it could be traversed if one wished to swim or paddle.

Cave Mistake, another of Cook's christening, is a tunnel in Becraft limestone, entered by a sinkhole on the Sosthenes Lawyer farm, one and one-quarter miles north of Russell Lake on the Cobleskill Road. A stream runs through it, and through a series of rockholes, into which farmers have thrown logs and sawdust to try to fill them up. This stream emerges at Becker's Hole, 3 or 4 miles distant to the south, and logs thrown in at Cave Mistake or just below it have been found at this hole, which is on the Becker Farm, near Cobleskill village.

Becker's Pond is a big spring, according to Cook, 80 feet in diameter, a bit over one-half mile south of Shutts' Corners. Not to be confused with Shutters' Corners.

Jack Patrick's Cave today is cemented up as a water reservoir for the owners, Mr. and Mrs. William Burke, and cannot be entered.

Continuing his survey, Professor Cook found a curious and rambling cave a short distance northwest of Howe Cave Village, which he has consented to have named Minister's Cave, for its local story. It is, or was to be, entered by a horizontal tunnel which led into a large chamber with an arched roof and smooth walls. A mere whisper here would give back echoes, and the story is that a local dominie used to go in here and practice his sermons, for the sound effects that he got as he orated. This is quite a relief from the numerous Devil's Dens and Devil's Holes that are scattered all over the country. There was an opening at one side of the oratory, very low and small, but it could be wriggled through to a passage in the shape of a V with one leg longer than the other. Its size and extent were matters that Professor Cook did not exactly remember, for his visit was over forty years ago. Later research, however, discloses that Minister's Cave, so-called, is actually Benson's Cave, half a mile, ten degrees west of the Barytes Mine, and could be entered once beneath the old portal to Howe Cave at the village, but no more. It is part of a cement mine, but it has an artificial extent of over 1,000 feet. It had stalactites in it half a century or more ago, but many had been smashed by vandals. Professor Cook found that the original passage doubled on itself in a peculiar manner, extending for over 600 feet almost directly against the dip.

The Van Voris party in 1928 found Benson's Cave entrance a rocky portal and for a short distance not difficult to traverse, but soon they were "spread-eagling" on shelves, straddling chasms above a lower passage where the stream had dropped down through and was flowing under a rock wall, boring its way slowly in a tunnel that required some wet-crawling, and again, leading to rifts, with the spread-eagle technique necessary. A pothole descent to another chamber, below, led to another, larger chamber with much debris piled up in a corner, half burying a fortunate find of a sapling ladder left by an earlier caveman.

Still a further passage tempted one man to creep through, and he found a fourth chamber with another pile of debris covering a continuing passage smaller than the last they had negotiated, which they had been told led to rooms containing beautiful formations, including rock crystals, but which they did not get to see. The great rush of water in spring, carrying in sticks, grass, roots, and other material had made rather a mess of this cavern, and the minister who used it as an oratory must have found it before the openings permitted so much waste to be carried in.

It was like being at the bottom of an open-topped silo in what Van Voris names Paul Robinson's Cave at Howe Cave Village, a perpendicular shaft leading to a first level about 25 feet down, but then comes a lemon-squeezer passage requiring the explorer literally to worm his way through, inch by inch, with elbows against one side and knees against the other, to get to the "true floor."

Here appeared two passages, one north, one south, the north passage leading along a waterway to a small pond with a ceiling so low that the crude box-like boat found in the water had to be propelled by lying down and pushing against the roof. An air current led to what was found to be another entrance to the cavern, with daylight showing through crevices, but the way had become blocked to human progress by rockfalls. Small formations were noted, and many jumbles of fallen rock.

Runkle Cave, in the Carlisle Center area, opens in a hillside and has two entrances, a creek inside, which flows with some volume at times, and a few fossils but no remarkable formations. It runs right through the knoll, as does the stream, the latter reappearing as a surface stream in a meadow. Just one of those casual caves of the Schoharie region.

Then there is Richtmeyer's Cave, which the state geologists explored and gave a very discouraging report about.

"It consists of a medium-sized room and a widened joint in Manlius which may be followed for 300 feet," said the early explorers.

But some roving spelunkers crept into it, and lo and behold:

"We may call this one Nameless Cavern, since it was so little known at the time of our first expedition and so fraught with difficulties that its wonders and beauties had been seen by few, and we know no other name.

"It is our belief that one of our group, our guide on this trip, was the first to fully explore the cavern."

What they found made Nameless Cavern known and got it a new name, for a few years later an energetic young man went to work on it and it is now "Secret Caverns," half a mile of its maze developed and cleaned, fitted with walks and lighted, its colorful formations glowing, reflected in places to double their beauty by pools of water and furnished with a waterfall at the far end, which is brought into play by turning an electric switch that opens the gate to a dam across a small surface stream. Roger Mallory, the proprietor, continues to extend his secret spaces and dreams of finding as many more underground wonders beyond the end wall as are now revealed to the visitors.

He makes no secret of his cavern, as many a signboard and newspaper advertisement are to be seen, day in, day out, tempting the tourist to detour off the main highway, up a steep hill, to the modest entrance building. You can picnic in a pretty grove at tables provided, and the fee is modest, if the advertisements are not. Some people will let their imaginations run riot when they describe caverns or caves.

For example, and to make a detour from Schoharie County, there is Sam's Point Cave, between Middletown and Pine Bush, a few miles northwest of White Plains. It was chosen by an advertising agency for an expedition sent there to test out an electric battery for flashlights, and here is the result, as it appeared in a full-page advertisement in a national monthly magazine:

SEVEN SKELETONS DEEP IN THE EARTH

*Amazing Escape of Edward Eisenkamp and His Six Companions Saved from Death in Underground Maze*

"Mile after mile we had wormed and twisted and crawled our way into the blackness of those caverns that burrow deep under the Catskills at Sam's Point," writes Edward Eisenkamp.

"Down at last to the very bottom, we relaxed for that moment of exultation every explorer seeks. And at that moment my flashlight slipped from my hands. There was a sickening splash and darkness closed over us.

"My heart pounded in sudden panic. We were trapped in a vast underground labyrinth, blinded by inky blackness. Trapped where only light could save us.

"Seven skeletons would grace this rocky vault Nature had prepared for us. What a grisly joke fate had played.

"But then we saw a glow of light from the deep, icy pool where the flashlight lay. We groped our way cautiously toward it . . . expecting every instant to see our beacon of hope fade and die.

"It didn't fade or die, or this story would never have been written. Fished up through eight feet of water, those fresh strong X Batteries maintained the brilliant beam that led us thankfully over the long, slow route to daylight.

"Until that day none of us realized how important fresh, dependable X can be. But we sure do now! For if those batteries hadn't been fresh, if they had gone stale on some dealer's shelf, they never would have brought us back from our near-grave."

Beneath a drawing of pale-faced men in attitudes of horror around a pool of water, two of them on hands and knees gazing into the icy depths of the water, and with an inset picture of an athletic young man, appears this caption:

> Edward Eisenkamp who with six companions had this thrilling experience in the Sam's Point caves in the wilds of the Catskills.

What shudders such an experience must bring to everyone who reads this! To think of seven strong men going into such a cavern with only one flashlight, in the first place—and walking "mile after mile" underground!

This adventure occurred or at any rate was published in 1936. Since that time Sam's Point Cave has shrunk terribly. It *must* have shrunk.

*"There is no place in this little cave, which is not over 150 feet long, where one is out of sight of daylight,"* comments Roger Johnson, who visited it in 1939. "Mile after mile . . .!"

Historian Simms tells of a small shelter cave in the woods about a mile northwest of Carlisle Village, where it is "believed Indians often found rest therein when visiting the neighboring settlements in the Revolution, as it afforded them ample security. Near it issues a fine spring. The bones of animals, fire brands and some 50 sticks, set in the ground, apparently for the purpose of drying meat gave evidence of repeated visitants, to those who discovered the place after the war."

Grosvenor's Corners may be underlaid with a large subterranean lake, in a cavern; at least one man, an aged member of the Grosvenor family, says that such a tradition was handed down by his grandfather. When the relator was a small boy, Van Voris quotes him, he was shown a rockhole in the rear of a cider mill in the village and told to keep away or he might fall in. Another aged man told the same narrator that he, as a boy, with others, had climbed down into it, with pine knots for lights and ropes to help them, and that they reached a rock ledge from where they could hear the roar of flowing water and see a sizeable stream and a lake, "an immense pool, so large it seemed to be entirely below the village."

Throughout the years the rockhole was used as a dump for the pumice from the cider mill, and other waste, and became well filled, overgrown with berry bushes, and unexplored until the Van Voris party tried to dig its way in. They did get into a pit some 12 feet deep, of solid rock, but could get no farther because of low ceilings and masses of rotting debris. They had to leave the tale to stand as interesting folklore of the region, with only the fact that some lengthy, low passages were seen.

Another "serpentine cavern," which Van Voris named Carlisle Center Cavern seems to be one of those narrow underground waterways which thread through this cavernous area and were traversed by early explorers and boys of the present generation for several hundred feet, but with much difficulty. Debris blocks some of the passages now, and exploring is considered hazardous because of so many low, confined adits and deep fissures in the floor. This cavern is located in a very small woods, two or three miles on down the road from the Ice Cave, and the nearest place to it is the village of Carlisle Center, in a region much cut up with clefts and ravines and potholes, indicating possibly that a large cave or series of them once existed here but have become closed or cut through by flowing water to become no more than ditches with a thin rock covering, or sometimes no covering at all.

One of the most intriguing folk tales of the Carlisle region clings to a rockhole which was said once to be an open and very watery cave on the Great Western Turnpike, not far west of Carlisle, and called Carlisle Cave by Van Voris. It might well be named The Dead Drover's Cave. It is on the Homer Hyney Farm.

In the early days of the settlement of the western or mid-states counties, the turnpike, known today as the Cherry Valley Road (U. S. 20), was the way by which cattle, sheep, turkeys and geese were herded to the markets in Schenectady and Albany.

These came from Ostego and Schoharie Counties, mostly, and drovers made good money taking the herds and flocks to be sold. The journeys were slow, taking some days, and the drovers frequented inns and taverns along the way, confining their charges in corrals or pens or barns for the night.

One lusty Dutchman who made frequent trips along the pike with large herds or flocks was reputed to be very wealthy; in fact, he was said to be fond of turning his smaller currency into large bills, and at a moment's notice he could produce a roll "that would choke a horse," or gold eagles that weighed down his pockets or bulged his money belt. A rough-and-ready, fearless fellow, he laughed at warnings from friends that some day he would regret carrying so much cash with him and displaying it.

One night in spring, during a long, heavy rain, he with his helpers stabled their cattle in the barn of Carlisle Tavern and put up for the night. During the night, because of the storm he became worried about the housing of his cattle, arose, and announced to one of his men that he was going out to the stables to see if everything was all right. He borrowed a lantern and went out—and that was the last ever seen of him.

The rockhole was at this time a veritable whirlpool, with surface water swirling into it. It was not far from the stables. The stream that went in did not reappear. The local tradition grew up that the Dutch drover was attacked, overpowered, perhaps murdered, robbed, and his body dumped into the maelstrom, whence it vanished, leaving no trace.

Another and happier folk tale is related by Paul Robinson, who has a cave named after him, as it is on his farm; but his best story is not about his cave, but Jack Patrick's, where early explorers used to find large deposits of quartz crystals, which were called Little Falls diamonds, from similar formations found at the town of Little Falls. A character who roamed the countryside, "bumming" most of the time, and with no particular means of support, appeared to have been the first to discover these formations and to provide himself with money when he was broke by selling them at the taverns and stores. No one was able to discover where he got them, although it was suspected he found them in some secret recess of Jack Patrick's Cave, at that time open and of considerable extent. Paul Robinson says some 400 feet of it could be negotiated at one time, until an earth-slide heaped up a mound of rock rubble right above the cave entrance, which hung there so precariously that entrance was deemed very dangerous. Perhaps it is best that this hole is walled up solidly and the water piped out for domestic uses.

A cavern quite recently discovered and explored is the McMillen Cavern, which is a four-mile motor drive from Cobleskill between Carlisle Center and Grosvenor's Corners. At last visit it was to be seen as a large sinkhole, surrounded by barbed wire to keep domestic animals from tumbling in. Van Voris and party found it, in 1928, "one of the most fascinating of the minor caverns of the county."

It has a semi-concealed entrance which suggests little of what is inside, but the good stout rope tied to a tree let the Van Voris party down exactly 53 feet from the surface to the floor of a chamber of considerable size, with adits that were crawlable on hands and knees—hip boots preferred, for there is usually some water in it. One tunnel, measured at 300 feet long, was coated with dripping amber-colored drops of water impregnated with the calcium of the dissolved limestone, for some distance; then came stalactites, large and small, and many of them, but no stalagmites to meet them, perhaps because flowing water on the floor prevented their forming.

At the far end of this tunnel the spelunkers had to dig away debris, again, and then came into a further chamber "truly magnificent to gaze upon." They found stalactites estimated to weigh well over 100 pounds each, in great masses, so beautiful that they were impelled to feel of them and pat them with their hands with care to break none off—and suddenly they came to a solid, high wall where the cave turned direction and led on to "the greatest thrill" of all.

They were on the verge of an abyss dropping from the rock

ledge into a large chamber which extended downward about 40 feet and upward about 60 feet, elliptical in shape, and forming a cavern of echoes, from the sound of their voices and of tossed bits of rock. Water came streaming in from all sides and flowed into the abyss below—and this was too much of a temptation. A rope over 100 feet long would reach bottom, and one of the most adventurous members of the group volunteered to make a try to reach it.

To do this he had to climb out over a crevice, rope in hand, with one end held by his companions, then slide down it, with his small flashlight held in his teeth, swinging back and forth in the waterfall.

Those above, snubbing the rope about a boulder, waited silently, not to cause him to drop his flashlight by trying to answer their questions, and with some relief, felt the rope slacken as he got footing on the floor below.

But the mist from the waterfall made it impossible to see him, though they could make out his flashlight beam, and shouted to him. He called back that he was standing in water 3 feet deep on the edge of a natural basin of rock that tapered off to unknown depth and that off to one side was another passageway similar to the tunnel they had come through above and water was rushing through it in a torrent. He tried to reach the entrance by holding to the rope and groping along the edge of the basin, but soon was in up to his shoulders in a strong current.

His friends shouted frantically to him to stop and come back before he drowned, and he obeyed, took a brief rest in the spatter of the waterfall, and began to clamber up the rope, hand-over-hand. It was no easy feat, with a wet rope, soaked clothing and falling water drenching him again and again as he swung in and out of the stream. At the very top he found it necessary literally to dive upward through the crest of the falls to get out of the crevice which he had descended.

The remainder of McMillen's watery cavern remains, probably, to be unseen until some modern equipment, such as a submersible suit can be used to follow the course of that deep, rapid river that must roar out in spring freshets with a mighty force.

McMillen Cavern lies not far from the famed Howe Caverns, to the north, and as in the case of other caves in the area, may sometime be found to connect with Howe Caverns.

Perhaps this may be the reputed Garden of Eden Cavern which Lester Howe is locally believed to have found after losing his farm and his cave at Cobleskill. The story is that Howe, embittered at his loss of the cave he had discovered, and which it appears he was unable to profit by with his arrangements, purchased another farm across the valley, called it the Garden of Eden and before he died, was believed to have discovered another cavern to rival Howe Cave—but that because of his bitterness and fear of losing that, he never told anyone where it was and died without revealing its location—or whether he actually had found such a wonder.

Nobody has been able to identify such a cavern as yet, although quite a few have tried.

The thunder and pounding of heavy machinery, grinding up rock to make cement, fills the immense hollows of the cement mine, at Howe Cave Village, close beside the Delaware & Hudson Railroad, which adds to the roaring sounds as long trains of coal and iron pass. The tall cliffs of limestone have been carved and smashed away by monsters of steel, and beneath the remainder a stratum of preferred Manlius was cut away, making an underground maze of vast extent, in which one could become lost. The great rooms, with sheer, smooth floors, and ceilings 8 to 10 feet high, lead to dark depths, and at one side into a dangerous rubble of fallen rock and broken timbers which once formed the entrance to the original Howe Cave, but now serve to plug it up completely.

Here, beside an old stone hotel building that is now the cement works office, a stairway leads down to a thick wooden door—and abandon all hope of getting into Howe Caverns by the back door. For the fun of it, we tried it, one hot summer day, led by the intrepid Roger Johnson, who so charmed the guard who was there to keep foolish persons out, that he just didn't see us drive in to a point near the yawning entrance of the quarry and then walk in. We clambered up the rubble-strewn passage as far as we dared, mischievously intending to surprise Mr. Clymer and Mr. Hall by sneaking in like boys under a circus tent. We had to retreat to the mine, stumbling over fossilized rocks, picking some up and pocketing them, thus plundering the cement company, which doubtless never missed them.

In the mine the grinding machinery of the cement mill shook the very rock above our heads until we found ourselves looking cautiously up at the solid ceiling, again and again. Nothing fell. We came out after walking for perhaps a mile around and around the many pillars left to support the ceiling, and drove up the hill, through Cobleskill, to the stone castle that is the entrance building of Howe Caverns—where we were welcomed and given the tour of the caverns as privileged persons, as we knew we would be, free of charge.[5]

The Sloughters of Schoharie Gulch may not be cavemen, but they come close to it; or they did until a few years ago. They are inhabitants of a remote rift in the rocks which are variously rent into many caverns and caves in this limestone-bedded county. They got their name from an English governor of Colonial times who was so cruel that his name became an epithet, forbidden to children.

Carl Carmer tells of visiting with one of the Sloughter clan in his yard before his hillside shack—a bushy-haired, sullen man who went barefooted, even when he came to town, and whose dull eyes brightened only when his dog was noticed, and then went sullen and silent as if ashamed of showing any sentiment whatever. The clan was once dominated by a rough old woman, Polly Scrom, and her name is perpetuated in "Poll's

[5] As with many other commercial caverns, members in good standing of the National Speleological Society are welcome to a tour, free.

Holler," and "Poll's Lib" or "Lib's Poll." The Sloughters have withdrawn from the civilized influences of the towns, huddling together in a shacktown of their own at Vroman's Nose, near the banks of Lime Kiln Creek, about two miles south of Middleburg. It is a sequestered place, shut off by nature from the rest of the world, seemingly shadowed after many generations by the sadistic spirit of Governor Sloughter, who had a man hanged for some trifling malfeasance, his name said to be Weismer, his history unknown, but with a faint tradition of having been a patriot whom the Tory tyrant persecuted, and whose descendants forever ostracized Sloughter's descendants and those of his followers.

## *Chapter X*

# THEY BORED A HOLE IN A HILL

HOWE CAVERNS was not built in a day, neither was the imposing rock building atop the hill, near Cobleskill; and no directions need be given here, for you can follow the signs and can't miss it.

This great cave, one of those mentioned by Carl Hovey in his invaluable *Celebrated Caverns,* was known, in times of Indian wars, by German settlers in the valley, but forgotten until rediscovered by cattle, seeking cool air on hot summer days, in a corner of their pasture.

Lester Howe was the owner of those cattle which constantly retreated to the shade of some trees in a far corner and were reluctant to leave. Howe went down there after them one day, impatient at their bovine stubbornness, and found out why they lingered. A draft of cool, moist air issued from a small hole out of which came a tiny stream. Mr. Howe, being an acute and curious man, looked into this thing.

The story is an oft-told tale, but true and worth telling again, of how the farmer got candles and went into what he did not dream was the largest cavern in New York State. It was eventually to be the means of making several fortunes.

One particular cow, named Millicent, is credited with having first found the cold air draft which came from the "River Styx" that flows through the caverns; but, curiously, the hole where Millicent stood was first found and used by a Jewish peddler in the 1770's, when he fled from raiding Indians and saved his scalp by hiding in the cave. An account of this event was first published in German, in a huge book in his native country, a copy of which is cherished in the Howe Caverns library.

However, it was Lester Howe who really made something of

his discovery in 1842. All alone, keeping his secret to himself, Howe made visit after visit into the dark cavern, climbing up, always a bit farther, with his feeble lights. Lanterns replaced candles after a time, until he had traversed at least a mile of marvelous passages, scrambling over steep, slippery rocks and oozing banks of flowstone, stumbling over unbelievably beautiful formations that were firmly bedded in the floor or had fallen and could be moved, one of them a stalagmite of such perfection it seemed to have been carved from white marble by an artist with Chinese tradition, and which today is known as the Chinese Pagoda.

Howe did not, by any means, explore all of this cave, but he became thoroughly acquainted with much of it and began to welcome visitors to it, for a small fee. Only torches and lanterns were used in Howe's time, no electricity being in common use. For a time its name was *Otsgaragee,* Indian language for "cave of great galleries"—evidence that the tribes of this area knew of it before the white men did; and bones found in the cave are believed to be those of some unlucky red men who had got in and could not find their way out. It would take an entire book to describe these greatest subterranean galleries in New York State—and there is such a book, *The Story of Howe Caverns,* published by the management.

It was "The Forest Parson," Rev. John Peter Resig, an exile from Germany, whose diary was responsible for the German account of a cave in America. Jonathan Schmul was the first white man to enter what is now Howe Caverns. He was not interested so much in its inner beauties and mysteries as he was in its promise of safety from raiding Indians, who were allies of the British. He had journeyed about, selling his wares, here and there, and was well informed of the strained relations among the Indians, British, and Colonists, and he warned Pastor Resig of the danger to the Schoharie Valley and took him into confidence when Resig asked him where he lived.

"I have revealed that to no one," answered the peddler, "but since you are a minister and can keep the secrets of the confessional I'll tell you. Ten miles west is a creek named after the German, Kobel, that is Kobelscreek. There I found a cave when the Indians were after me. That's my home. But be mum about this. Should war break out, then flee to this cave and you will be safe."

The ancient chronicle, first published in Germany, then in St. Louis, Missouri,[1] states that Pastor Resig was called upon to visit a sick woman who "lay in the Cavern which was dimly lighted by a candle."

Later, after he had evidently spent much time in the cave, he emerged to hasten to the scene of the Battle of Oriskany, one of the bloodiest of the early conflicts of the Revolution. He arrived just as Chief Brant was pointing out General Herkimer to his braves, urging them to kill him. Some of the warriors made a dash for Herkimer, and Pastor Resig sprang to his side, seized a battle-axe, and defended him.

"A fight more embittered, more shocking, more horrible, than that part of the Battle of Oriskany, when men threw their weapons aside in a hand to hand encounter and strangled their enemies to death cannot be conceived," he wrote in his diary.

After the wars had ended, the cavern was evidently forgotten or deliberately kept secret by the few who knew of it, but prior to 1842 there began to be talk of a mysterious "Blowing Rock" on the side of a hill north of Cobleskill Creek, where cold air issued on warm days from crevices in a ledge, but no one, within the memory of the oldest inhabitant, had investigated the cause when Lester Howe, a newcomer to the county, began to speculate about the cause of this "blowout" of cool air.

On May 22, 1842, after observing how his cattle kept close to the hole in the wall, he began his investigations. He had to cut away a cluster of bushes to get into the small entrance. He fastened a tape at the entrance and unwound it as he proceeded into the astonishingly lengthening galleries and tunnels. He was finally halted by an underground lake, now known as the Lake of Venus, but persisting, dragged in wood, built a raft and

[1]*Der Waldpfarrer am Schoharie*. Eden Publishing Co., St. Louis, Mo.

Typical travertine in a New York State cavern

A wedding in old Howe's Cave, 1854. Lester Howe's daughter marries in her father's underground bridal chamber, where some 32 weddings have since taken place

crossed the lake. It was a voyage of an eighth of a mile, and he landed to clamber on, up and down, over the "Rocky Mountains" and into the inner depths of the cavern.

Howe's discovery became a nine-day wonder, was featured in the newspapers of the world, and studied by geologists, one report being published in 1843 in Part 1 of the *Geology of New York*.

Named "Howe's Cave," it was visited by growing numbers, its story published in geographies, natural histories, encyclopedias and special books on caves.

Lester Howe grasped the opportunity to make some money out of his find. He opened it to the public at fifty cents admission, provided special clothing, including rubber boots, and curious oil lamps like inverted funnels with handles, one of which has been preserved to this day.

It was no easy trip, this rough, wet, sticky journey of more than a mile, including a tipsy voyage on a raft, and much risky clambering up and down heaps of slippery rocks, and sometimes wading in the bed of the stream, but later the area at the foot of the lake was lighted with gas, a small, narrow-gauge railroad was built, and a hotel erected. The Albany and Susquehanna Railroad came through in 1865 and crowds began to visit Howe's Cave.

One of the most spectacular stunts put on in Howe's Cave was the marriage of Lester Howe's daughter, H. Elgiva, to H. S. Dewey, in a room which was and still is called the Bridal Chamber. Miss Elgiva must have been an agile young lady, for she had to climb a long ladder in her trailing wedding gown. An ancient photograph taken of the event, on September 27, 1854, shows the pair standing before the parson—who also wore a long white gown—holding hands in an obvious statuesque pose for the photographer, with attendants dimly seen by the light of flaring torches and lanterns. Two roughly dressed men with lanterns in hand are climbing the ladder like visiting firemen.

Many a wedding has been held here since. Whether it was

Elgiva or not who furnishes one of the best guide stories that are told in the modern Howe Caverns, the present management swears this one is true:

A young lady who had made the statement that she "wouldn't marry the best man on earth" had a change of heart when she fell deeply in love, and managed to keep her vow and be married by having the ceremony performed in the Bridal Chamber, which, she said, was not *on*, but *in* the earth! As this account is being written, a total of thirty-two weddings have been held in the Bridal Chamber.

Two of the hotels were burned down, a third one partly destroyed by fire. The third hotel was air-conditined, in part, by the ingenious Lester Howe, who forced the cool air of the cave into the dining-room on hot summer days, thus becoming perhaps the first man to make use of such a natural cooling plant. But in the 1880's the Howe Cave layout began to go into decline, and the Howe's Cave Association was formed. Lester Howe sold out to them. This new management also failed to prosper, and the cave was closed to the public.

In the early days of the century some southern caves were beginning to use electricity for lighting, and Mr. John Mosner, of Syracuse, who knew of Howe's Cave and had visited it after it was closed, got an idea. He revisited some Virginia and Kentucky caverns which had electric lights, in 1927, and came back to organize a corporation to improve Howe's Cave.

The proposed improvements were somewhat startling. Mr. Mosner proposed to the subscribers of a half-million dollar corporation that they *bore a hole in a hill* for a new entrance, install elevators, and build a stone castle of sorts atop the hole in the hill, pump out mud, lay brick walks, build bridges, and provide an elegant boat ride on the Lake of Venus, everything to be electrically lighted.

The plan called for a very elaborate—and experimental—engineering project, but the corporation decided that "there was gold in them thar caverns" if they could be made more easily accessible and interesting to the public.

H. A. Homburger, civil engineer, and one of the firm of Smith, Golder and Homburger, Inc., of Saranac Lake, started studying the Mosner plan. He discovered that there was no sort of official or unofficial information available as to just where the caverns did run under the hill that rose above Cobleskill. He made a trip in rubber boots and flashlights through the original entrance in January, 1928, and estimated it might take two or three weeks to make a survey. It took three months. It was desired to construct the new entrance at the far end of the caverns from the old one. Without going into detail, it was accomplished by boring a test hole where surveyors and engineers had designated—and the drills came through within three inches of the spot where the engineers had marked, deep down in the cavern, that it ought to emerge.

The engineering work, including electrical installations, took eighteen months, and the new Howe Caverns was opened to the public May 27, 1929.

Since the management of Howe Caverns has carefully compiled its entire story and published it,[2] we shall not pirate the book any more than we have so far, but will merely say that now two twenty-passenger elevators take visitors down a shaft 166 feet below the surface and let them out to be guided through one of the most beautiful underground areas in the world.

One of its new-grown features, due to the introduction of strong light, is the green algae or fungus that appears under and near most of the electric flood-lamps. From germs or seeds that had lain dormant in the darkness for unknown ages, there sprang up this green growth of several species, but the bats that used to hibernate here do not like light and so many human visitors, so no longer visit the caverns.

A typical holiday trip to and through Howe Caverns was made by some two-score spelunkers, many of them members of the National Speleological Society, who came to study the geological and other interesting scientific features of these and other

[2]*Story of Howe Caverns,* compiled and edited by Virgil H. Clymer.

nearby caverns, May 31, 1941. You wouldn't know the old place, now. There is no mud, the walks are cunningly surfaced and sloped, the Bridal Chamber is a clever grotto with an inset of translucent rock in the shape of a heart for the bridal couple to stand on while being married, and with broad stairways instead of a shaky ladder leading to it, and the many almost bewildering formations have been cleaned and beautifully lighted. The climax of a guided trip is a boat ride of an eighth of a mile during which you see the moon rise, the stars come out, and the comets streak in Fourth of July colors across an underground sky.

The coloring of the caverns is in many areas most delicate, in pastel tints and shades, ranging from bluish to golden. They lend themselves admirably to color photography, as was demonstrated for publication, first, in 1941, when I did an article for *The Saturday Evening Post,* which was illustrated in kodachrome. The photographs were taken especially for this article, with increased electric installations to step up the lighting from 20,000 to 40,000 watts. The scene used by the *Post* was of what is probably the most interesting mass of formations in the caverns, a long, sloping bank with massive stalagmites rising from it, and hangings of flowstone, travertine, and other colorful and fantastic shapes, making it resemble an underground rock garden. The colors come from the dissolution of various minerals or soil which becomes incorporated with the limestone and water that builds the formations, age after age.

These developed caverns furnish a very interesting study for the geologist, the brilliant lighting making their studies easy. The cavern was formed in the ever-present Manlius of the region, with a roof of Coeymans, which yields more slowly to erosion. An exhaustive survey of the original Howe's Cave was made in the early 1900's by Professor John H. Cook, assisted by James F. Loughran, as his surveyor, and Harry C. Cook, photographer, and maps were drawn of a part of the cave.

One of the most fascinating features of the modern caverns is the Winding Way, a narrow passage that makes two dozen turns in the course of a few rods, ending in a small adit called Fat Man's Misery. This tortuous channel is paved with bricks laid so as to permit one to know in what direction he is going.

At one point in the Winding Way there hangs a slab of pure quartz, above the heads of passers. It is translucent, and a powerful electric light placed above it brings forth a beautiful rosy glow in the rock.

Other attractions are virtually endless in these caverns, and the management has named them well, or permitted visitors to name them. Some have had their names changed several times, but the rather unromantic name of Howe clings to this virtual underground empire that stretches through the hill for one and one-half miles of known distance, with the possibility of there being other adjacent caverns behind the rock walls of the developed portions. No effort has been made since 1929 to open them and develop them. Enough is enough.

## *Chapter XI*

# LOST CAVES

WHEN you go looking for a lost cave you will have a lot of fun trying; perhaps you will find it, and when it is a combination of a lost cave and a lost pond, you have something to hunt for.

Up in the Adirondacks, northwest of Ticonderoga, is Lost Pond. There is a cave which was called Lost Pond Cave. It is no longer lost, for we found it. Part of it, however, is lost as a cave. It is the part between the beginning and the end.

The expedition was designed to be a mountain climb and a cave crawl, plus a hike to a secluded little lake in the Adirondacks known as Grizzle Ocean. This lakelet is in the midst of a State Forest so new it hasn't yet been named. It is reached via the tiny settlement of Chilson, on N. Y. 13, about fifteen miles from "Fort Ti." Rain, wind, and clouds turned the would-be mountain-climbing program into a cave crawl, with an outdoor supper and, for me, an indoor breakfast to end all breakfasts, during what we city folks called post-war starvation.

Led by William Endicott, chairman of the Albany Chapter, Adirondack Mountain Club, with the able assistance of A. T. Shorey of the Lands and Forests Division, New York State Conservation Department, a party of nine drove from Albany to the home of Forest Ranger Alex Stowell at Chilson and asked for further guidance. Alex, a native of Stowell, gave it to us. He had been in Lost Pond Cave in his youth and he had all the folklore about it.

Lost Pond Cave is in the heart of what was once the private hunting preserve of Stephen H. E. Pell, genial and well-informed owner of Fort Ticonderoga. Treadway Mountian, the principal objective of the "Cloud Splitters," was shrouded in clouds so thick that it was useless to try to climb it for anything other than an exhausting clamber.

An old road, once used as a long-haul logging road from Pharaoh Mountain cuttings to Ticonderoga, was passable by car to Putnam Pond, a sizable lake about two miles in, where it became a rough trail, over which the hikers trudged with their loads of duffel including tents, sleeping bags, food, fishing equipment, etc., to an Adirondack shelter at Grizzle Ocean, named from an old trapper who had once made it his headquarters and facetiously gave it the name of "ocean." A tiny, pretty pond in a hollow, ringed by evergreens, it was also in the Pell preserve until fifteen or sixteen years ago, when it became state property, but had not been developed as a public camp site as yet.

Since the shelter was designed to house only six persons, and only one of the party felt like tenting on the damp forest floor, arrangements had been made to have the guest spelunker housed at the Ranger's home after the outdoor meal at the shelter. A return hike to Putnam Pond, part of it made in darkness, settled his supper well. The Adirondackers, piling onto their "brush bed" of spruce browse, huddled in early to escape the rain which grew to a torrential storm during the night, and the Treadway Mountain project was regretfully abandoned when morning showed all the mountain peaks completely obscured in clouds and mist.

At ten-thirty a rendezvous at "Put" Pond, a drive back to the former gateway of the Pell Hunting Lodge area, and a half-mile hike, brought them to Lost Pond. En route, exploring limestone ledges and gullies, an interesting cavern was found with a stream emerging from it. It was explored for some 50 feet up the stream and "surveyed" with lights some 50 feet further in where the roof came very low to the water.

There are three entrances to this lower cavern, openings in moss-grown limestone, joining inside, one of them very picturesque, and later a careful tracing of the underground stream in the gully revealed that the stream comes from Lost Pond, and that these lower openings must be a continuation of the upper cavern, which was found with little difficulty, close to the outlet shore of Lost Pond.

No surface water flows from the pond; it seeps into the ground and rock and does not appear in the upper cavern, which proved to be a true, "live" cave, with several adits, grottoes and passages, some joining. Its total crawlable extent is estimated to be about 150 feet, and an added 100 feet of low-roofed cavern extending on to an unknown vanishing point over a deep bed of soft sand which evidently had been washed in by surface waters long ago, filling the passages to a depth of several feet in places. Considerable spade work might enlarge this cave so that it could be explored much farther and made comfortable for walking about upright in its larger portions. It is curiously carved by water and chemical action, with odd "banks" and "terraces" in the side walls; the roof perfectly flat for the most part, and glistening with drops of water and calcium or silicate. A geologist in the party, Dr. E. E. Barker, analyzed the rock as crystalline limestone with traces of graphite. The sandy floor was littered all over with the droppings of porcupines and out of them grew tiny white fungus and mould; in one small adit was a pile of the manure where it was evident a family of porkies had huddled, but none were found in the cave on this day.

Very tiny stalactites were found, queer "knobs" of rock here and there, and in a grotto too small to be entered, a twisted column, a combined stalactite-stalagmite about a foot long, some flowstone and, in places, lively flow of surface water from cracks, making it a very live cave indeed.

From Ranger Stowell came the story that at one time, years and years ago, this cavern could be crawled clear through from the upper entrance to a lower one. Evidently the lower caves, from which the stream emerges were once to be reached from above, an estimated quarter of a mile distant. No other caves, but several large and small sinkholes were found in the vicinity.

A legend of buried treasure surrounds Lost Pond and nearby

areas; indeed, two of them. One has to do with an old Indian who inhabited the area and used to emerge now and then with some silver coins, sufficient in value to keep him in provisions so that he did not have to work; and "provisions" included a bout with firewater now and then. This was along in the early nineteenth century or even before 1800, according to Ranger Stowell, who got the story from his father, a native of the area. A family by the name of Barber that lived at or near Chilson started a search for the Indian's hoard, said by some to be of Spanish coinage, and by others to be "silver bars" from a "lost mine." Three generations of Barbers hunted in vain for this lost treasure; the third, George Barber, returned periodically after he had removed to Vermont, but died without discovering such a cache, nor has anyone else found it.

But the legend of silver ore to be found in the mountains nearby persisted, and one Adolphus Lavigne was said to have discovered a mine or cache of bullion but lost it and died without ever finding it again. This was supposed to be on Putnam Mountain, across the valley.

The Lavigne prospecting occurred about Civil War times, Ranger Stowell thought, and it was at this period that extensive logging was carried on in the Pharaoh Mountain forests, and as many as two hundred teams would be hauling lumber out on the Chilson–Putnam-Pond–Grizzle-Ocean–Pharaoh-Mountain road, delivering it at Ticonderoga where it was loaded on barges and shipped by canal to Albany for reshipment by Hudson River boats. The current pay was five dollars a day for man and team—a twenty-four-hour day, most of the time. The hauling was done on sleighs in winter. The logging has now been reduced to some desultory pulpwood cutting in the Chilson area, which is the center of an old grant known as the Stevenson Grant, mapped in 1832 as containing a house or two and a school. The Stowell house, the oldest yet standing, a store and post-office, some farmhouses and buildings now form the settlement, which is traversed by lively brooks and fringed by small lakes. The background, to the west and south is the Putnam Range, named for Israel Putnam, who was born near here and fought Indians and French in the mountains and at the forts at Ticonderoga and Fort Edward, etc.

The former Pell preserve now contains a beaver dam, backing up water over a large swamp from the old logging road, easterly; and another small pond is formed on the Lost Pond stream by an earth-and-rock dam near the hunting lodge that still stands and is owned by a private individual. It is to be reached by car in dry weather.

Some strange "dikes" of rock and earth run parallel to this road and cross it, and Ranger Stowell said that the earliest settlers could not account for them; in places they are 5 feet high and 6 to 8 feet wide, with huge boulders in them.

One guess at their origin and possible use is that they were built to form a "flow" for logging operations, that is, to dam up water to float logs across and drive them downstream; but Mr. Pell scouts this theory, and unless there was an immensely greater water supply in the earliest period of logging here, than now, such an operation would have been impossible. They must remain a mystery of the Lost Pond area.

Mr. Hal Burton, a New York City writer, who has a unique lodge on a hill overlooking the Keene Valley, tells of a lost or perhaps entirely mythical cave on the side of Nippleton, in the Adirondacks, said to be a man-made one, a silver mine dug by some Spaniards who grew fabulously wealthy and then vanished. Probably some of "Coronado's children," far, far from their usual haunts in the southwest. Burton says that every hiker who bushwhacks up the trailless south face of this peak, overlooking Elk Lake, hunts for the reputed cave or mine, but none have ever found it.

Jane McCrea's Cave is a total loss. The strangely persisting tradition that this unlucky girl, who was captured and slain by "Gentleman Johnny" Burgoyne's Indian allies in the French and Indian Wars and hidden in a cave near Fort Edward, where she had gone, all dressed up, to meet her fiance, David Jones, a Loyalist officer, has been debunked time and time again. It has been historically proved that Jane was killed, scalped, and her body left lying in the woods, very shortly after she was captured —but her massacre had much to do with the fierce resistance made by the patriots of upper York State to the British general's ruthless hordes of red men, and his red coats, besides.

Lost, also, is a treasure cave, up in the Adirondacks, "half-way up Mount Colden." This treasure has been elsewhere located by legend, but has never been found, any more than Captain Kidd's wandering cache of piratical plunder which has been sought for at an enormous expense, all the way from Maine to Long Island and points up and down the Hudson. Harold W. Thompson credits Henry van Hoevenberg, a talented eccentric, with "remembering things that never happened" in order to locate what appears to have been a British paymaster's trunks of gold coin, intended to pay off the soldiers, but hidden by Algonquin Indians in the so-called Halfway Cave on Mount Colden. To add to its value, there was wampum mixed with the money. Van Hoevenberg actually found the cave and the treasure, he related, but was surprised by the "ghost of an Algonquin guard" which was so good a wrestler that it tossed Van over the edge of a cliff some five thousand feet up, his fall broken by soft pine tree branches, and he survived, with only two broken legs, three broken ribs and a fractured arm, but with his pockets full of gold and wampum.

There is a real cave that is lost in the vicinity of the Alleghany State Park, somewhere; that is, it is lost to white men but not to the Seneca Indians; one white man who is known to have been there cannot find it again. A. T. Shorey, of Albany, was taken to this cave one dark night, blindfolded, by some of the Senecas whose reservation he was visiting, and was permitted a glimpse of a yawning hole in a cliff, fringed by dense foliage. He heard the Indians praying and going through some secret ceremonies. Shorey understood that the cave was a sacred place, tried to register his surroundings in his memory, but the only light was from flickering torches, and when the ceremonies were over he was blindfolded again and led away. He afterwards made a vigorous search for the cavern in daylight but never found it.

He did find the Cave of the Little People, not far from the town of Salamanca, in the same vicinity, and proof that it really is for little people only is furnished by the fact that this accidental shelf shelter in the rocks is but a few inches from floor to ceiling. This also is a sacred place for the Senecas. It is on the road between Quaker Bridge, New York, and Bradford, Pennsylvania, in the park, near a famous spring. All Indians pass it with reverence. "Old John" Jimson showed it to Shorey.

"When we were passing it on the road," relates Shorey, "he asked me to wait a minute while he paid his respects and said some sort of Indian prayer. This is hardly a cave; more of a small grotto."

The "Little People" were discovered by a little boy who set out to hunt squirrels, as related in some of the legends collected by Carl Carmer. They had a sacred place on a cliff, and when the lad shot a black squirrel it fell at the feet of some of the little men who were so tiny they could not even pull out the arrow and only had strength to carry the squirrel which the boy gave them. He lugged two others, gray squirrels, to their home, where he was welcomed and fed and taught the ritual of the *Djogao,* a race possessing supernatural powers, and this ritual he taught to his own tribe under the direction of the *Djogaos* who were invisible to all others save this boy.

"Even to this day the Little People are known to be near the spot where the boy first found them," Carmer relates in *Listen for a Lonesome Drum.* "Often in the silent woods beside Cattaraugus Creek, the beat of little drums may be heard and then the Senecas know it is time to sing the songs and hold the ceremonial."

There are a number of caves which were lost because of being closed by an earth slide or cave-in, or by some curmudgeon who did not like to have spelunkers invading his property to visit the cavern or caverns. Such a one is described by D. C. Robinson, the owner of Knox Cave at Altamont, as a Skull Cave, because of some mighty startling things that are supposed to be in it.

Mr. Robinson has been trying to clear up the mystery of Skull Cave for some time and has been writing to me about it since 1943, when he furnished the following account:

> This story has come to our attention. Sixty-three years ago the man who told it to me helped his father and others draw a large boulder to close the mouth of a cave. The owner of the cave could not keep people off his property or from going through his crops.
>
> This man told us that he went into the cave, which was extensive. The only thing that made a lasting impression on him was the first large room. On the floor of this room, partly covered with clay, he counted twelve human skulls and a number of skulls of cows. These cows were not like any he had ever seen, as the horns were about twice the ordinary size, next the head. The walls of the room were covered with pictures and writing (that) he could not read, cut or scratched in the rock.

There is some evidence to support his story, not much. . . .

On May 5, 1944, Mr. Robinson reported that the owner, with whom he was negotiating for purchase or lease of the cave, had "not signed the necessary contract to permit development of the cave said to contain the skulls."

Mr. Robinson had elaborate plans for the development of this mysterious wonder—whose location he does not reveal—but on May 24, 1944 he wrote:

> I got a new proof of existence of the cave "Skull Cave." An old lady says that when she was a child her aunt used to talk of sitting at the entrance in hot weather because it was cool there due to air from the cave.

At about the same time Mr. Robinson reported that the walls of Skull Cave are said to be covered with sign writing or "hieratic characters like those used in Egyptian writing," and that:

> The Latter Day Saints, or Mormons, say that they are like the early writing of the Nephites and are probably one of their records which were written in a modified form of Hebrew language in a modified form of Egyptian character. (I get it as Hebrew shorthand in Egyptian signs.)

We were now being offered an opportunity to go into the development of this cavern on a cooperative basis, to provide work for the postwar world, to make money for ourselves and to establish a tenth wonder of the world in the way of a cavern that had been the tomb of a drove of longhorn cattle that were being driven up from the Rio Grande by a squadron of Mormon cowboys over the underground railroad.

If you have friends who like to gamble, I like to gamble, too,

The temptation was almost irresistible, but time flew by and on September 16, 1946, a report of progress came through.

> Mr. M. W. Stirling of Berkeley, Cal., tells me to report any such finds as may be in *Skull Cave and experts will be sent to conduct necessary excavations and proper study.* (Italics are his.)
>
> We are so slow in getting a start at Skull Cave that one of the men I consulted is dead and I think a second one also. There are very few left who knew of the cave and its closing.

And finally, in November, 1946, Mr. Robinson gave up. Unable to make a deal for this Golgotha of a cave, he wrote:

> I doubt the truth of the story but do know that owner closed the entrance to stop the public crossing fields through his crops. *That indicates something.* (These italics are mine.)

But we are getting closer and closer.

> The land is so located that one can see Schenectady and part of West Albany with area between. View is fine. There is ample water, fine picnic area, etc.
>
> Using the story properly for publicity and offering a good cash prize to the first patron who finds or makes a usable entrance to the cave, using the barn as office, concession and museum and charging a 25¢ fee to enter grounds, the farm will pay for itself, if cave is a hoax.

Do we have any bids? Come, all ye spelunkers, get your skulls together and let's go digging for those buried skulls—if Mr. Lewis, the owner of the property will permit. There's the rub!

Knox Cave, itself, which is one of the older commercial caverns, has been leased by Mr. Robinson to two veterans of World War II, the Weber brothers, who by prodigous labor have refitted the cavern with stairways, hand-rails and other safety devices, after it had been closed during the war and had gone into some decay as to man-made interior fittings. Spelunkers who visited it during its closed season, in winter, found the entrance a mass of ice and almost impassable, but very beautifully decorated by the iceflow, which seemed almost to imitate the rockflow inside. Its principal feature is the Rotunda Room, a sizable chamber, 110 feet from floor to ceiling, but it has some calcite crystals and cave onyx, fossils, and other interesting wonders which have made it a center for study by groups from schools and colleges for many years.

The history of the cavern provides a mystery, according to Mr. Robinson, which may be four hundred years old. The discovery of a stone tablet in 1934 with "hieratic writing" on it, causes him to believe that the cave was used by people preceding the Iroquois Indians, who later used it for many years and left artifacts scattered about. In early Colonial times Dutch soldiers pursuing Indian marauders from Fort Orange, now Albany, 18 miles to the east, discovered that the vanishing Americans were vanishing into this cave.

"Added attractions" at Knox Cave are free picnic grounds, athletic fields, and grand views of the country, but to many experienced spelunkers the interior has proved disappointing, perhaps because they had been led to expect too much by the somewhat imaginative descriptions provided by the owner; but still it is a good cavern and well worth visiting, as commercial caverns go. It has been left in a more natural state than some, and although well lighted and paved in rough places, there has been no shifting of formations or building of rooms by man. The visitors enter on the second and third levels; there are 6 levels that have been traveled, and more than 9 parallel sets of passages, and a rumor that there are 4 other rooms connected with the main cavern which have not been broken into. These may be called lost caverns until some intrepid spelunkers make a break for the one-hundred-dollar reward offered to the person or persons who manage to find them.

Another lost cave, supposed to be between Spencerville and Austerlitz, but its exact location and its name, if any, forgotten, is reported by residents of the vicinity to have been shut off by a rockfall. There are a number of these closed or lost or forgotten caves scattered about the Empire State, which should furnish fine hunting for the growing numbers of spelunkers. As this book is being written, a sudden, spontaneous and active interest in spelunking has sprung up, with especial, eager exploring activity by Boy Scouts seeking new worlds to conquer in their outdoor program.

Most likely, many a cave overlooked in this literary survey will be found and added to the growing index of Americans caverns that is being compiled by the National Speleological Society. There is always the chance, in known cave country, of discovering some tiny hole, some underground stream or spring which leads to a cave. Such an area is that in the Lebanon Springs country, and Canaan and Hudson. There are limestone springs scattered about in Rockland County, one of them reported to be "gaseous," which may mean sulphurous, and near the line of Canaan Township, on land once owned by a Mr. Lord, a small stream sinks in and reappears, obviously having cut down into limestone and carved a channel for itself. There are the Sharon Springs, too, typical of the Helderberg drainage system.

Mather, in his *Natural History of New York,* published in 1842, refers to these springs and holes, and tells of such inviting—or uninviting—caves as the Spook Hole, near Barnegat, Dutchess County, "a small cave in limestone; but it is said to have so much carbonic acid gas as to make it dangerous to enter, without precaution.

"Lights burned well at the time of my visit. I saw nothing of particular interest. It is about one-half mile southeast of Barnegat and at 50 to 70 rods to the Hudson River," he says.

Mather also discovered two small caves in Cornwall Township, Orange County, near Round Pond, about four and one-half miles southwest of West Point. One, he set down, "is described as the roof sparkling with brilliant crystals of spinelle,

Entrance to Mohonk Caves

Found! Lost Pond Cave, Chilson, N. Y. Formerly it was open for a quarter-mile

Bonaparte's Cave on Green Pond, St. Lawrence County

A station on the underground railroad. Hough's Cave near Lowville

High in the Helderbergs, Livingstone Cave, at High Point, Altamont on spelunker ladies' day

mica, arigite, hornblendes, etc. It is now filled up at the mouth so as to be inaccessible.

"The other is called Bear Hole and is about one-quarter mile southwest of Round Pond, a small, circular mouth, scarcely more than large enough for a good size bear to enter. Would be a fine winter retreat for these animals."

There are myriad "lost mines," containing either gold or silver, copper, or some other precious or semi-precious metals, such as the Lost Tinker Mine, described as a silver mine on Dunderberg Mountain, down the Hudson at the entrance to the Highlands. Its story, in brief, is that a land-going pirate used to store silver in the cave or fissure each time he sailed up the river and went ashore, taking two men with him to dig it in, then slaying them, so his secret would be kept. And one time he failed to return to his cache and it has remained lost ever since.

Another example of this sort of thing is a rock-shelter formation on the east end of Belden Mountain on the trail from Piseco to Spruce Lake, where "an old-timer found gold, opened a tunnel and worked it for several years coming out each Fall with a load of ore in a tramcar. On his last trip out he did not bring the car with him but left word in Piseco that anyone who wanted the car could go and get it, as he was not coming back. This was around the year 1875."[1]

Dr. R. H. Flower has searched in vain for a reputed large cavern in Fort Ann, located somewhere near a small shelter cave in dolomite, that he did find. Going from Comstock to North Granville, there taking a road to the north and following it to the last house, he climbed the side of a mountain to the shelter cave, then hunted around the shoulder of this mountain for the big one which a Mrs. Steves at a farmhouse had told him used to be visited by people. It may be there, if one believes, as in fishing, that "where there are little ones there are big ones," but, so far as we know, it is lost.

Caves get lost not only because of cave-ins and earth slides,

[1]Related by A. T. Shorey, who had it from local residents of the Piseco region.

but because of the growth of forests and thickets that conceal them.

Another lost mine, with a long Indian legend connected with it, is celebrated now and then by some news writer. Arnold H. Bellows, of West Hurley, revived the tall tale lately of the Lost Lead Mine of Teunis, the last of the Catskill Indians, who had a secret store of lead in a cave somewhere in the vicinity of an ancient Indian village called Pakatakan, which the early Dutch settlers changed to Teunis, also naming a lake after the village and the Indian who had the same name. The story is that Teunis, in his old age, promised a friendly white man, a Mr. Bassett, to take him to the mine, if he would go blindfolded, which he did. Teunis also promised to reveal to Bassett the exact location before he died, but died suddenly without keeping his promise.

Years later a cave was discovered some miles from Teunis Lake, but no lead was in it, and still another cave was found near Arkville village, with artifacts dating back some five hundred years, according to Attorney R. S. Ives of Roxbury, who unearthed them. The cave and Indian earthworks nearby will soon be inundated by the deep water of a big reservoir to be built at Downsville to augment the water supply of New York City.

## *Chapter XII*

# HIGH AND LOW IN THE HELDERBERGS

THERE has probably been more extensive and intensive study, by scientists, of the Helderberg caverns, some low and deep, some high and dry, than those in any other speleological area in New York State, rivaling even that made of the adjoining Schoharie County region to the west.

The great wall of varied limestone which rises along the border of Albany and Schoharie Counties is a paradise for rock climbers and a school for geologists. All seek and find many things, including fossils galore. The rock wall is honeycombed with caverns and underground drainage systems.

Best known in Helderberg cave country is the Thacher Park playground, and the best known cavern is Hailes' Cavern. The latter has also gone under the name of Sutphen's Cave and Thacher's Cave, but the name of the original explorer has persisted. He was T. C. Hailes, a vigorous pioneer who literally left his mark in or on more than one cave in this part of the country.

Hailes' Cavern is visited by a constant stream of persons. It has been seen, from the outside, at least, by thousands, though not commercialized for many years. It is one of those "at your own risk" challenges. It provides possible plunges into icy water up to the neck.

Professor John H. Cook, in his careful survey, reported:

> . . . several caverns exist at the base of the Manlius limestone between Altamont and New Salem, but because of the limited area draining them, have not been developed to a size that renders them accessible, and only one was found large enough to enter.

> This is known as Sutphen's or Thacher's Cave and is the property of John Boyd Thacher of Albany. . . .[1]

It must be explained that this account is over forty years old, but it is the best official survey account extant and has been checked and rechecked by its author and experienced spelunkers who have explored it within recent years, and found quite accurate.

Professor Cook gives the total extent of this cavern as 2,800 feet, and describes it thus:

> (The cavern is) located at the base of the cliff beyond the alcove north of the Indian Ladder Road, and most conveniently reached across the fields back of the house (then) occupied by Mr. Albertus Hallenbeck, or near the top of the "Ladder."
>
> The passage for the first 530 feet is broad and low with pools of water at intervals. The general direction of this first section is north, 40 degrees, west. Then for 750 feet the cavern is a high, narrow joint running north, 35 degrees, east toward the face of the cliff. At the end of this section the incongruous legend *"farthest west!"* has been painted upon the wall. The remainder of the cavern averages two feet in height and twelve in width, extending irregularly to the northwest for 1603 feet, beyond which it is impossible to go. A small branch which leaves and returns to the main passage, something over 600 feet from the farther end, is clear of clay and fragments and high enough to permit one walking in a stooping position. For this reason it is named "COMFORT LOOP," the comfort being purely relative.

Professor Cook and workmen did a considerable job of draining some of the deeper pools in the cavern, but, according to later explorers, there is plenty of water to wade in, and the use of a boat and submersible suits is advised for complete exploration.

Hailes' Cavern is in the custody of The American Scenic and Historic Preservation Society, as agent for the state of New York, but there has long been some dispute about the ownership, as the shelf in front of the cave is claimed by the owner of the adjoining property. The land above, on the surface, is

[1]Professor Cook says that Hailes' Cave was also known as Helmus Pitcher's Cave in the days of Patroon Van Rensselaer, and it may be that this was used by the Anti-Renters of the Helderbergs for a hideout.

within the park for about 200 to 300 feet, as the cave runs underneath, but beyond that the cave and branches are under private land.[2]

The danger in Hailes' Cavern is not at all imaginary nor due to claustrophobia. A girl, "skylarking and falling off the lower shelf, was killed," according to a letter from the late Raymond H. Torrey, secretary of the Society; and a party of students from Rensselaer Polytechnic Institute, Troy, entered the cave in 1933 and, their flashlights fading, were lost and remained in the cave in considerable discomfort all night, until another party went in next day and got them out.

The Helderberg cliff area is altogether so interesting, geologically and historically, that it has been studied over and over by successive generations of scientists, historians, and nature lovers, and geological literature contains many references to the area. It was the chosen haunt and pathway of Indians, from which comes the name Indian Ladder; it saw something of the unrest and rebellion of the Anti-Renters, and of the so-called Helderberg War, when a mob of 1,500 indignant farmers, in revolt against the Van Rensselaer rental system, or its annual "tribute" that had to be paid by farmers who had bought patents from these patroons, forced a sheriff's posse to retreat to Albany.

It has been the hiding place of fugitives. Near Hailes' Cavern is the Tory Hole, a cave about 25 feet wide, a sort of shelter, sometimes known as Tory House because it was reputed to have been a meeting place and refuge for the Loyalists of the region. John Salisbury, a British spy, was tracked here and captured at about the time of Burgoyne's campaign which ended in the latter's surrender at Saratoga in 1777. Smoke from his fire, issuing up a natural chimney, betrayed him.

The geology of the Helderbergs has attracted probably two dozen scientists from many lands to study it. They have come from France, Switzerland, and from many states, colleges and museums in this country, and the names of many of them ap-

[2]From a Report of The American Scenic and Historic Preservation Society, 1935.

pear on the tablet at the top of the old Indian Ladder Road, erected by the D. A. R. in 1933.

The most recent guide to the subject is *Guide to the Geology of John Boyd Thacher Park,* by Winifred Goldring, M.A., Assistant State Paleontologist, New York State Museum, Albany, available from the Museum, where Miss Goldring still presides. It is interesting to know that the Helderberg Escarpment is believed to have proved a bulwark against which not even the glacial drifts were able to do much damage, although the ice did plane off the plateau at the top.

For a change to high and dry caverns, there are two at High Point, right above the village of Altamont, which have a long and colorful history and, as caves, are typical of many of the mountain-top caverns which have survived for millions of years.

A recent spelunking expedition organized by LeRoy W. Foote, of Middlebury, Connecticut, an officer of the N.S.S., took some two dozen panting, scrambling persons to the summit of High Point in the spring of 1946. The party was guided by two "human antelopes," A. T. Shorey of the State Conservation Department, and Darwin Benedict of the State Department of Commerce.

After a tough crawl in and out of watery Clarksville Cave, the Yankee spelunkers, from Massachusetts and Connecticut, making their first spring trip of the year, were met at Altamont by their guides, fresh as daisies, and drove in cars from the railroad station, abruptly uphill on N. Y. 156, off on a dirt road past Seminary Shrine, to the former home of Judge Peckham, a member of the State Supreme Court. The then unoccupied house was made the starting point for a real hike which included mountain climbing, rock climbing, falling down, boring through dense brush, and tripping over loose rocks and each other, as we did a side-hill dodger stunt, clinging close to the sheer cliff and going halfway around the High Point bluff, which rises almost 1,000 feet above the village.

There were, here and there, enticing openings in the cliff, but they were by-passed as mere rifts in this crumbly, breakable limestone. We came, finally, to a fine *porte-cochere* sort of entrance, with fairly safe and easy stone steps leading up and the portal leading into a tunnel. This is Livingston's Cave, evidently named after the family of one Azor Livingston, as C. M. Warner, of Altamont, local historian reports it.

Anyway, as a high, dry cave, Livingston's was and is to be recommended—but there is no need of making a side-hill dodger of oneself to get to it. Boy Scouts had blazed a trail by an easy ascent to the top of the plateau, leading first to a cave-opening like a pot hole, right in the level surface of the glacier-planed plateau, then on to a point where descent could be made, with a short rope tied to a tree, over the edge of the cliff and down into the handy *porte-cochere* entrance to Livingston's Cave.

Our guides had a reason for taking us up the hard way, as will be seen later. This cavern is a tunnel that branches three ways—west, northwest, and southwest. Small formations appear, including one tiny grotto high in the wall of one passage, with a single white stalactite hanging in it, unbroken, probably, only because it was not to be reached by vandal hands. This is still a live cave, despite its height, with some small dribbles of water forming dripstone on the walls in a few places.

From the interesting portal, a grand view is to be had of the lush country to the east, south, and north, only surpassed by that from the edge of the escarpment above and a bit to the north of this cave—a scene that our guides had saved for the last by taking us up the hard way.

Curiously, this cavern, within a few yards of the other, has no such human history as Wynd Cave (variously spelled Winn, Wynn, Win, Whyne, and Winne), according to Mr. Warner. But Wynd, pronounced like "wind," is the name most used today. Mr. Warner's research, which he says was prompted by my inquiry, turned up something of a robber's-roost saga, the details of which had not been known before, although the cave has been called the Wynd Brothers Robbers' Cave.

Mr. Walter Pier, who lived near the Wynds and attended the same school as a boy, furnished most of the story.

In 1887, two of the Wynd family were convicted and sentenced for the robbery of Elam Williams' store and postoffice at Knox. The family was not native to the region but came from far away, and first lived in a house near a crossroads tavern, known as Brumaghim Corners, near Knox, then moved to Thompson's Lake. Here, Lewis (or Michael) Wynd, the father, tried to support a large family, including three sons—William and Charles, who later got into trouble, and Jesse—and daughters Jane and Evelyn. The land was poor and, although Lewis shod horses, he had to work out as a hired man.

It appears, also, that he was a roamer, hunting and seeing quite a bit of the wild country along the Helderberg heights, and thereby stumbled upon the upper cave at High Point.

Thereafter, he spent much time removing loose rocks and debris, and with lumber that he toted up on his back, through the woods, built a cover for the entrance, with a slanting door like a hatchway door to a cellar, and put a padlock on it.

His purpose was to attract summer boarders and city folk who were beginning to frequent Thompson's Lake as a resort and, by charging admission, make some money.

Wynd did not own the land where the cave is and did not even bother to ask permission to take it over, and just before the Fourth of July, when he expected to guide many parties to the cave, he paid a last 'lone visit and found his entrance shed smashed and the cave mouth full of loose rock piled on the broken lumber. That spoiled his scheme for profiting by tourist trade and, although he visited the cave himself and removed the rock and reopened it, he never rebuilt the shelter.

It was after this that Lewis Wynd began to "dig for gold," either as a one-man-mining effort or, as a member of the Whipple family, near whose property his operations were conducted, tells us, "he was burying money." A large hole in a field of oats that was found one day helped to support the belief that there was buried treasure of some sort concerned, and this legend has persisted. The spot was ideal for such a yarn to grow, being "close behind a cemetery."

At about the age of forty-six or fifty Lewis Wynd died suddenly—from the kick of a horse, it is thought—on a nearby farm where he was working.

"At this point the credible and smooth-flowing saga of the family seems to end abruptly," comments Mr. Warner, "and from then on, begins the era of hazy, fragmentary, legendary exploits of the younger Wynds, which followed the immediate departure of the survivors of the family from their home to parts unknown."

But William and Charles Wynd, who had gained a poor reputation as young ruffians while still in grade school, and who had soon "gotten too big for book learning" and quit school, drifted back to the region around their old home. They were seen now and then, here and there, under the usual "suspicious circumstances" that cover a multitude of innocuous doings—or sins—and their seeming lack of steady occupation led to the belief they were thieving. It seems that at intervals they were even reported to the sheriff who would muster a posse and chase them, but they always eluded capture and were supposed to hide and live in the cave atop the plateau.

Finally came the forced entry to the store in Knox, and because it housed the postoffice, pursuit was more vigorous. One of the lads was caught, after suffering severe exposure from fording ice-choked streams and plowing through deep snow. The other, discouraged, was found one morning in front of a store awaiting capture. Convicted and sentenced, one died in jail, and thereafter they were forgotten, except for the cave with its story of buried stolen goods, which remains as a memento, not only of the Wynds, but of another quite respectable and interesting character.

Theodore C. Hailes, if he did not actually discover the cavern in the Thacher Park area, did publicize it and seems to have been a scientist. He was sometimes called professor, and whether it was a title of courtesy or he held a degree, he was an instructor of some sort, perhaps of speleology, at the old Albany High School, then on Columbia Street.

Hailes left his mark, in red and white paint, on the rocks of some of the caves that he "discovered," or near them. He painted his name in red, high up over the Indian Ladder cave entrance, and, curiously, as if to prove beyond a doubt that he had gone clear to the very inner end of the Wynd Cave, he daubed in white paint on the face of a rock, invisible save from a tiny, low grotto into which one must squirm and coil around like a snake, to face outward, the inscription:

T. C. Hailes, 1883

It was reported, also, that at one time there was another inscription in this cave, reading:

Two men buried here, 1778

But we lack confirmation of this, and since the Altamont Boy Scouts have chalked or painted numerous inscriptions on the rocks about the region such as, *"Welcome splunkers,"* (their spelling), the cavern graveyard idea may have been theirs. Theodore C. Hailes and his field work, to some extent, first called attention to the curious natural features of the Helderbergs, and in the early years of the present century this interest became so widespread that Mr. Warren says people in Paris and other foreign cities knew about them when they did not know about the city of Albany, itself.

The area around Thompson's Lake is natural cave country, and the underground outlet for water from Hailes' Cavern was known of as far back as farming was carried on in the region, later proven by Professor Cook's explorations. Several sinkholes, disappearing and reappearing streams, rifts, crevices, and at least one "bottomless" cave are more or less known. One is an unsavory hole, "abreast the Gallupville road, a rockhole into which dead carcasses, unwanted baled hay, and the like have been dumped for generations and they just fall out of sight."

Near Thompson's Lake a man had a well that was none too wet and decided to deepen it in hope of striking a better vein of water. While so digging, a part of the bottom of the well fell away and the tools vanished. The digger didn't go after them. Local farmers know of many of these "rockholes" but are much averse to entering them or encouraging anyone else to do so. Those who do enter usually find themselves blocked at some point by deep water.

Thacher Park itself, besides its well-known points of interest, including Hailes' Cavern, every now and then reveals another "rockhole" or cave, and Mr. Warren points out a tiny one located above the Bearpath Walk along the lower edge of the escarpment, awkward to reach and scarcely ever visited.

Vincent J. Schaefer, who suddenly burst into prominence in the scientific world in the early autumn of 1946 by creating "artificial snow," has gone spelunking about the Helderbergs and has made a careful study of some of the caves. In a broadcast over WGY, Schenectady, June 5, 1946, during the General Electric Science Forum, Mr. Schaefer told of the Witch's Cave, or Witch's Hole, near the little settlement of Helderberg on the road to Beaverdam, as follows:

> Local tradition tells of an old witch who lived near the little settlement of Helderberg on the road to Beaverdam. Among her reputed capabilities was the power to enter her cabin and without visibly emerging from it, she would suddenly come from the woods some distance away. Again, according to tradition, when she died, a search of the cabin showed a trap door above a large cavern. From one corner of the cavern room, a passageway could be followed for some distance to a place where it emerged in a secluded glen.
>
> If this story is true, the witch certainly would rate high in her abilities as a spelunker. In order to negotiate her alleged route, we found it necessary to go through several rotations in a horizontal plane during the course of which we were completely plastered with mud from head to foot. Her ability to get through without disclosing her secret by her appearance would call for a considerable degree of magic power.

Mr. Schaefer, in his field work in the Helderbergs, found that formations such as stalactites are not common. One reason for this "is the collecting instinct inherent in most of us. While some are content with a small piece of flowstone found in the rubble on the floor, others are not content unless they emerge with the biggest and best formations that could be broken off.

In this respect, there is a common fallacy that such formations grow at a constant rate. Some large stalagmites were broken off many years ago in one of the rooms of Benson's Cave, northwest of Cobleskill. When I found the evidence of this over-enthusiastic action, it was apparent that several had been removed at the same time. Natural forces immediately started to repair the damage but it was evident that the rate of growth was far from a uniform process. New growth more than a foot long has formed in one location, while alongside a second deposit had built up only a few inches. The rate of build up of stalagmites is, of course, directly related to the quantity of water and its dissolved minerals which reach a particular spot and are deposited when the water evaporates."

Mr. Schaefer's exploration of the Helderberg caves was partly stimulated by his hope that he might find remains of ancient man in them.

"It has always been one of our ambitions," he admits, "to locate a *dry level* room which had been occupied by the early inhabitants of America. This possibility was given considerable impetus when the tooth of a ground sloth was found in the Gebhard Cave at Schoharie."[3]

Not a single trace of prehistoric man has ever been found in these northeastern caverns, however, and probably never will be, although the remains of many mastodons have been found scattered widely about New York State.

Mr. Schaefer's interests, ranging from his research at the G. E. Laboratories, as assistant to Dr. Irving Langmuir, to crawling into "rockholes" in search of prehistoric man, and also to study

[3]R. Veenfliet, Jr., of Schoharie, brought to the State Museum at Albany a tooth and fragment of bone which he found in the bed of a small stream in Gebhard's Cave on land owned by him near Schoharie. The fragments were sent to the United States National Museum ((Smithsonian Institution) for determination, and referred to Dr. C. L. Gazin, Assistant Curator of Paleontology. He reported:

"A more specific determination of the *tapir* tooth and the bone fragment is not feasible. However, it is possible that the form *Tapirus Haysii* (Leidy) is represented, as this species is recorded from the Pleistocene of Pennsylvania, Indiana and other states farther south from New York. I know of no other record of tapir from New York State."

the growth of formations, including "ice stalagmites" in the Tory Hole, finally led him to get high up above the earth in an airplane with a quantity of dry ice which he dropped into the clouds hovering above Mount Greylock, Massachusetts, to produce the first man-made snowstorm in history. This is going from low-low to very high, as man goes, but we do not need artificial snow over here in the Berkshires at all, save for impatient skiers who may wish to fly on wooden wings out of season.

We earthbound spelunkers met Mr. Schaefer, the "snowflake scientist," on the expedition to Mount Hope Iron Mine, previously described, and in that old mine he was quite fascinated by what might be called "semi-artificial fog," for the horizontal shaft of the mine, open at both ends, one entrance very large, was filled with dense fog from the ingress of warm, humid air from outside to the very much cooler atmosphere inside, which was the exact reverse of Schaefer's method of making snow by hurling dry ice into the clouds from above. But you can see what spelunking sometimes leads to!

Perhaps it led Mr. Schaefer to go higher, for he concluded his radio address, quoted herewith, by saying that "the present inhabitants of caves on a permanent or visiting basis—spiders, blind fish, crickets, toadstools, porcupines, bats and spelunkers—seem to be satisfied with their choice, since most of them can go and come as they please. Let's leave them alone and find a way to get along with our neighbors all over the world on top of the ground.

"Even *I* don't want to *live* in a cave!"

He was referring to the dreaded possibility that we may have to retreat into caverns deep under earth to escape atomic bombs, if another war comes.

But there are a few men and women, too, who have lived in caves, at least temporarily, and not too deep down.

## *Chapter XIII*

# INDIAN AND INDIAN FIGHTERS' CAVES

NOT only Indians, but white Indian fighters resorted to caves, in pioneer days. At least two historic holes have been named out of James Fenimore Cooper's books. One is called Natty Bumppo's Cave; the other, Cooper's Cave.

Curiously, although the hero of the Leatherstocking Tales was a fictional character, the cave named for him appears to be real, so real to the people of Cooperstown and vicinity that a controversy arose over whether it was one or another. That was settled by referring to the writings of Cooper's daughter, Susan Fenimore Cooper. She was closely associated with her father in his literary work and she wrote *Pages and Pictures,* in 1861, which included a drawing of Natty Bumppo's Cave.

This is "indisputably the one of early tradition," declares Ralph Birdsall in his *The Story of Cooperstown.*[1]

On the other hand, another controversy sprang up about the actual character upon whom Cooper is supposed to have based his leather-stockinged hero, whether it was Nathaniel Shipman or David Shipman.

The "official" Natty Bumppo's Cave is about one mile from the village of Cooperstown, high on a hill that rises from the eastern side of Otsego Lake. It is a steep climb to not much of a cave, for it is hardly more than a cleft in the rock, but in *The Pioneers* Cooper used novelist's license to enlarge it into a romantic and respectable cavern.

Then, in 1909, a larger cave was discovered, lower down the

[1]Scribner's, 1925.

hillside, with an entrance in the woods, beyond Kingfisher Tower, and beyond Point Judith. This touched off the argument which Susan's book and drawing appears to have settled.

But along comes the story of Nathaniel Shipman, of Hoosick Falls, a leather-stockinged woodsman, who was a close friend of the Mohican Indians, fought with them against the French and the Canadian Indians, became a hero of these wars, but turned neutral during the Revolution because of his friendship with both sides.

For this he was tarred and feathered by his own neighbors and vanished from his home.

Judge William Cooper, father of Fenimore, was responsible for Nathaniel Shipman's being found by Cooper's son-in-law, John Ryan, of Hoosick, who had seen the man haunting the shores of Otsego Lake, a hermit of sorts. He was an old man, had been missing for twenty-six years; he was returned to his home in Hoosick Falls, but he never forgave the neighbors who had so humiliated him and he frequently returned to Cooperstown. However, when he died, he was buried with honors in Hoosick Falls and celebrated as the original Leatherstocking. The Cooperstown people denied this, favoring David Shipman, who was no relation to Nathaniel, and when a movement was started in 1915 to erect a monument to Nathaniel at the Falls, the Cooperstown residents indignantly referred to him as "the spurious Natty Bumppo."

David Shipman was interred in a cemetery between the villages of Fly Creek and Toddsville, and his grave was marked in 1900 by a stone erected by the D.A.R. He had served in the American army as a member of the 114th Regiment of the Albany County Militia in the Revolution. After the war, he settled in a log cabin on the east bank of Oak's Creek and was known as a man of the woods, tall, slender, wiry, dressed in deerskin, moccasins, and long leather leggings to his knees, and carrying a squirrel gun with a long barrel, with which he killed plenty of game and supplied the Cooper family with deer and bear meat.

One may take his choice, or be neutral, but from the close assocations that David had with the Cooper family, it would seem that he had inspired the character of Leatherstocking—although Cooper may have rolled both these pioneers into one, and he may have used both caves to create his cavern.

Natty Bumppo's Cave, as "certified," is on the Vision, a rock ledge overlooking the Susquehanna, near Templeton, where Otsego Hall was built, the home of Judge Templeton in Cooper's story.

Here it was that Elizabeth Templeton and the old Mohegan were surprised and surrounded by a forest fire. They were discovered by her lover, who also was caught in the fiery circle, and they were about to give themselves to death together in the flames when Natty Bumppo appeared and guided them to safety on a barren rock above the cave which fire could not reach.

The cave was used as a sort of fort by Natty Bumppo and his aides against an attack by a posse of "more or less military makeup," and as Cooper painted the picture:

> The troops now divided, one party being led by the Captain, over the Vision, and were brought in on the left of the cave, while the remainder advanced upon its right under the orders of the lieutenant. Mr. Jones and Dr. Todd appeared on the platform of rock immediately over the heads of the garrison though out of their sight. . . . The besieged had drawn together a pile of black logs and branches of trees, which they had formed into a *chevaux-de-frise,* making a little circular abatis in front of the entrance to the cave. . . . The long and much dreaded rifle of the Leatherstocking was seen issuing from the parapet and his voice cried aloud:—
>
> "Keep off! Billy Kirby, keep off! I wish ye no harm, but if a man of ye comes a step nigher, there'll be blood spilt atwixt us."

Natty threatens, if pressed hard, to blow the roof off the cave with gunpowder. After some battling in which only Squire Doolittle's trousers were nicked in the rear by a shot from Natty's rifle, Judge Templeton appears, and Oliver Edwards and Major Hartmann, and:

> . . . they reached the terrace in an instant, from which the youth

The Devil's Hole or Massacre Cave

The Gorge Cave near State Park

Harris Hill

NIAGARA FALLS CAVERNS

Typical bat colony on roof of a cave

Sitting upside down is no trick for a bat, and this one seems comfortable

led the way, by the hollow in the rock, to the mouth of the cave, into which they both entered, leaving all without silent, and gazing after them in astonishment.

They find the aged, half-demented "Fire-Eater" in the cave, the lost Major Effingham, a Tory whose property has been proscribed and himself hunted, but was now to be restored, and his grandson, Edward Oliver Effingham, Elizabeth's lover, made one of his heirs.

Here is more than a suggestion of the persecution of Nathaniel Shipman, it would seem.

The cave was also a counterfeiters' hideout, according to Cooper, who described it as "a secret receptacle of guilt, and as the rumor of ores and metals found its way into the confused medley of conjectures, counterfeiting and everything else that was wicked and dangerous to the peace of society, suggested themselves to the busy fancies of the populace."

There is hardly a smaller hole in all York State with taller tales about it than Natty Bumppo's Cave, and the Cooper's Cave at Glens Falls must take a back seat in this respect.

Traces of Indian shelter caves are remarked along the Delaware River, above Port Jervis, with some pottery fragments as the chief artifacts. Nearby are The Lifting Rocks, a curious cavity formed by a huge flat slab supported on legs of stone.

The Lifting Rocks are atop Hawk's Nest Mountain, off Hawk's Nest Road, and the formation consists of a huge slab of rock held up by three stone legs, forming a shelf or slit into which a man might crawl sidewise. The story connected with this curiosity is a rare one.

An Indian named Cakhoonzie was captured by the English, as a child, and sent to England where he was educated. Some shrewd traders took an interest in the lad and sent him back to this country, his destination New York City, his errand to deal with the Indians for the traders and get the best bargains in furs. But Cakhoonzie had other ideas. When the ship he was on neared port, he dived into the sea and swam ashore. The scents of the forests from which he had come lured him and he did not wish to be immured in the city. He made his way to his homeland and found that his entire tribe had been exterminated by the fierce Delawares.

Cakhoonzie fell in with Tom Quick, noted Indian slayer, who hated the Delawares like poison. The two joined hands to kill as many Delawares as they could. They camped on Hawk's Nest Mountain where they had a splendid lookout over the surrounding country, as many a cloud splitter had observed, in climbing to the Lifting Rocks.

One day they saw a war party of Delawares approaching. The party landed and walked down the bank of the Neversink, evidently bent upon fishing.

Cakhoonzie and Tom Quick swiftly smeared the Lifting Rocks with pitch and heaped dry wood all about them. Tom Quick then sneaked down and around below the Delawares and at a signal, which consisted of smoke from the fire that Cakhoonzie started at the Lifting Rocks, Quick also set a fire in the forest. It swept up the stream, and Cakhoonzie tipped over a round boulder that had stood close to the Lifting Rocks, and was red hot from fire, and rolled it down through the woods. It ignited the dry forest as it rolled, the Delawares were caught between two forest fires and wiped out.

Cakhoonzie was one of the last of the Narragansetts, or the Podunks, who were the only members of King Philip's federated tribes to survive and who escaped by fleeing far into the Adirondacks, to settle about what is yet called Podunk Pond.

At the lower gorge of the Niagara River is a cave with a satanic name and a gory history that has been permanently preserved by the Niagara Frontier Land Marks Association.

This is the Devil's Hole, a rugged chasm in the bank of the river, about three and one-half miles below the Falls, on the American side. It is from 100 to 200 feet deep. Overhanging the cavern is a perpendicular precipice, from the top of which falls a small stream, usually dry in summer, and named Bloody Run.

The perpendicular cuts in the rock, geologists say, were caused by an arm of the Niagara which flowed into it just after the glacial period. From the Devil's Pulpit a long winding stairway leads to the ravine and the Devil's Hole, a cave in the rock 30 feet deep.

At the entrance is the Ambush Boulder which in past ages, to judge from its size and contour, must have fitted perfectly into the doorway. The interior of the cave contains many peculiar excavations dimmed by time, attributed to a pre-historic race.

According to one Indian legend the cavern was the home of the Evil Spirit. Another legend has it that La Salle explored it in 1679 and heard a mysterious Indian voice prophesy his death to take place years later, on the Mississippi.

The cave was the scene of the Devil's Hole Massacre during the French and Indian Wars. On the morning of September 14, 1763, John Stedman, keeper of the local portage, and a wagon train of 24 men was ambushed by a party of Seneca Indians. Men and horses were driven over the cliff and only Stedman and one or two others escaped.

Two companies of British soldiers stationed at Lewiston hastened to the rescue but fell into another ambush. Sir William Johnson, military commander for the district, reported 5 officers, 64 privates killed, in addition to the civilians in charge of the wagons. The anger of the Indians had largely been aroused by their fears that they would lose the business of carrying supplies around the portage to the wagon trains that were beginning to traverse the area. Previously, freight went by boat and canoe up the Niagara River and the Senecas were employed to carry the loads around the portage made necessary by the falls.

On September 13, 1902, 139 years afterward, the Niagara Frontier Landmarks Association unveiled a tablet at the spot. The inscription reads:

At the top of the Cliff, Above This Spot
September 14, 1763, Occurred
THE DEVIL'S HOLE MASSACRE
Where 500 Seneca Indians Ambushed a
British Supply Train, Massacred Its Escort
And Hurled Bodies and Wagons Into the Chasm
Below; Only Three, John Steadman, William Matthews,
And One Other Escaping.
Erected by Niagara Gorge Railroad Company
And Presented to
Niagara Frontier Landmarks Association
1902

Down at Dover Plains, near where the Appalachian Trail crosses from York State to Connecticut, is the Stone Church Cavern, one of the most picturesque places in eastern York State. Nature, here, has built an arched chamber of Gothic architectural suggestion, much resembling a man-made temple. It has a waterfall at the rear, and a brook tinkles through the chamber, which is not too much of a cave to explore, but the surrounding rugged terrain provides miles of rock climbing up the steep sides of a glen or gorge, and along the brook, which is pitted with potholes, here and there, and several pretty waterfalls.

The Stone Church is "ribbed and walled by massive rocks whose arched opening resembles that of some old-time place of worship," as an old Blue Book describes it.

It was once the sanctuary of one of the last of the Pequots, Sassacus, a chief of the tribe, who with some of his followers, took refuge here after the defeat and practical annihilation of his people by Captain Mason in the Pequot War. Coupled with scenic beauty, the difficult clambering which the area affords makes it a goal for many a "Cloud Splitter" traveling the Appalachian Trail, as well as others who can motor near to it, on N. Y. 22. It has been surveyed by spelunkers galore, one of whom, Ned K. Anderson, of Sherman, Connecticut, a leading mountain hiker and cave explorer, guides bus-loads of his young followers to it, now and then.

## *INDIAN AND INDIAN FIGHTERS' CAVES*

A modest metal sign beside the main street in the center of the little town invites visitors who motor along the main highway, to take a path that leads through a double row of beautiful Norway maples and across grassy fields passing limpid pools of spring water, to the Stone Church Cavern, not ten minutes' walk from the highway.

Here, in a cliff that rises some 100 feet from the meadowlands, is an opening exactly resembling the arch of a Gothic church or cathedral, from which issues a seething stream of water that stays cold all summer, and which roars down a waterfall 60 to 70 feet high at the rear of the immense cavern, which is 60 feet long, 26 feet wide, and 30 feet high, with a narrow opening to the sky in its roof of schist rock. Flowing water has carved out this natural temple.

In winter and until late spring the cavern is decorated with great masses of milk-white ice, with bluish tints in it, forming ice stalagmites and stalactites, draperies, and many odd forms, which are repeated on the walls of the cliff outside. In mid-summer the temperature is never above 65 inside, that of the water about 62.

There are Indian caves, later used by lumberjacks, on the Northville-Placid Trail, between West Canada Lake and Cedar River Flow. This is a section of The Long Trail of New York, which extends for 136 miles. Near these caves runs, also, the Old Totten & Crossfield Line, one of the oldest land lines in the state. It crosses just west of Cobble Mountain. The nearest road is sixteen miles away, but the loggers swamped out timber and made wood-roads and used some of the shelter caves as blacksmith shops. Hunters also used them and still do, and thereby hangs a tale that is familiar to the Forest Rangers of this wild area.

One summer, a young couple appeared at a Ranger cabin and said that they were so sick of city life that they wished to be directed to one of the remotest places from civilization that they might find, but where camping would be good. They wished chiefly to fish and bathe and go boating, to climb about and hike through the woods and not see another living soul until they had become thoroughly rusticated and cleansed of the stains of the metropolis.

A Ranger directed them to one of the large shelter caves, five miles from his cabin, and they packed in and made camp and stayed all summer. Toward the end of the season, the husband went trout fishing down a stream, as he had done numerous times before, but this time he did not return as it grew dusk and the wife, worrying, and knowing how rough the stream-bed and shore was, walked five miles to the Ranger cabin for help. The Ranger had departed on duty, the cabin was locked.

The by now desperate woman smashed in a window, crawled in, and telephoned to the Ranger at Speculator, who immediately started a search for the lost hubby.

In the meantime, hubby had found his way to the trail and was on his way to his cave home, not going near the Ranger cabin where his wife had remained. When he reached his wilderness home, he found his wife missing and immediately hastened back to the cabin, five miles away. He did not find her there, and now, as desperate, or more so, than his wife, he phoned to the Ranger at Piseco, who also started a search.

The hours passed—and the husband returned to the cave hoping to find his wife there—and he did. He had taken a loop in the trail to the cabin when he hurried to it, while his wife had returned by another part of the same trail, and in the darkness they had passed within a few yards and missed each other.

The sequel was that they paid seventy-five dollars for damages to the Ranger cabin and the time and efforts of the two searching parties. It is believed that they got entirely rid of their anti-city complex, about this time, although they did not immediately leave their cavern camp.

There is a cave on Kitty Cobble, a mountain that rises 3,200 feet above sea level and is a wild and rugged projection of rocky land. It has a faint tradition of having once been an Indian cave, but is better known as Kun-Ja-Muck Cave, the chosen hideout of one, French Louie, whose real or true name was Louis Seymour.

Born about 1870, French Louie was a trapper and hunter who definitely preferred to be alone most of the time and who was known to have a secret hideout somewhere on Kitty Cobble, as well as one that was not so secret, part way up. The story *The Mystery of Kun-Ja-Muck Cave* is told at book length by George F. Tibbitts in his volume by that title—but if you are looking for a description of French Louie's retreat you will not find it in the book, and it remains somewhat of a mystery still. Except that the ubiquitous A. T. Shorey has visited it. It is an eroded hole, forming a sizeable room in a difficult, hidden place, to be reached only by a sure-footed person who is not afraid to crawl and claw his way around a bulging ledge on a narrow shelf, or to drop down to it from above.

The story is of a city man, Gray, who was "driven to the wilderness" for health of body and mind. He is led to spend months in a search for the "mystery," which turns out to be a couple whom French Louie was harboring in the cave, fugitives who did not need to hide after all. This provides most of the plot of the novel. But French Louie was real.[2] Periodically, he would appear in the town of Northville on the Sacanadaga River at the foot of what is now Sacanadaga Reservoir, and proceed to blow in most of the money he got for his furs, on drink. But he was always almost foolishly kind to children, and gave away some portions of his cash to any child or group of children that he met. Before he died, in 1915, Louie reformed and seems to have been a much beloved character, a kindly cave man who had been his own worst enemy.

Probably there is no more romantic an Indian cave in the east than that known as the Kiantone Cave or the Cave of the Elixir Spring, which is to be found in the Allegheny Reserva-

[2]Mr. Shorey says that all the characters in Mr. Tibbitt's novel were real persons, under fictional names.

tion of the Seneca Indians, close to the Pennsylvania border.

It appears to have been, originally, a small natural cavern from which gushed mineral water which the Indians considered a cure-all for many ills. Old Corn Planter, the sachem of the tribe, is said to have brought the sick and old here to be cured and made ointments from the sediments of one of several springs in the vicinity.

Then along came white men, who seem to have been as superstitious as the red men, and began to dig a tremendous hole at the outlet of one spring, and who, according to Edmund S. Carpenter, writing in *New York Folklore,* "believed they would find two books of gold, whose yellow pages held the secrets of all mortal illness." One of these books was to give the recipe for an elixir that would cure any disease in the universe.

Mr. Carpenter, an archeologist, visited the place in 1941 and found a massive oaken door in the mouth of a tunnel which had been cemented on walls and roof, and he and his party used a power-pump to drain the tunnel, which measured 3½ feet wide, 4½ feet high, and kept descending to lower levels, the first one 60 feet below the entrance, and another of unknown depth.

A newspaper account in 1858 told of the excavation in progress, at that time, and said that the tunnel ran 171 feet into the hill and descended at an angle of 20 degrees. It was first exploited when a spiritualist brought some of the "magic water" to New York City.

John Murray Spear, a Universalist minister, turned spiritualist when an analysis of the sediment promised healing properties. He immediately organized a movement to establish a new order on this earth, to be known as the Kiantone Spiritualistic and Communistic Community. This was to become an Utopian city of grand edifices; it became a hut-town of octagonal shapes, a holy place where pilgrims came, and from whence issued tracts that made converts and led to the announced invention of a perpetual-motion machine by Spear, which was to draw for its power "on the magnetic life of Nature."

At a convention attended by some 20,000 persons from as far away as St. Louis, a formal excavation was started to find those magic golden books and buried treasure of other sorts, but no such treasure was found; and after a mob had invaded the convention, in anger at alleged free-love rites, the colony degenerated into a ghost town.

The whole story of the Kiantonians is too long to relate here. Their "great city" is now just a rubble in the wilds, but the springs still flow, one of them, at least, being of ill-tasting sulphur water, the Kiantone spring clear and sweet. It formerly lay within the state of Pennsylvania, by the survey of 1787, but a new survey placed it just north of the 42nd parallel, which forms the southern boundary of New York State, now, at this point. There is a sort of spiritual radioactivity yet remaining about the ruins, some say, and it is at times haunted by the ghosts of Indians, come to renew their lives, and by mysterious manifestations of nature such as rolling fireballs—and now and then is visited by a roving "believer" who comes to gather up the influence of the magic spring.

## *Chapter XIV*

# BANDITS' ROOSTS AND HERMITS' HOLES

Most notorious of the guerilla bands that harassed the countryside all up and down the Hudson in Revolutionary War times were Claudius Smith and his cohorts, who haunted and gave name to Claudius Smith's Bandit Cave, located in wild country near Tuxedo Park.

According to the many reports that have been written about Smith and his gang, there were two caves that he used, one to shelter his horses and one to live in and hide plunder, and from whose mouth he could look down onto the turnpike and spy out slow-moving stages or convoys coming along, then mount and dash down by a short route to intercept them and rob them.

The cave where he kept his horses has given a name to Horse Stable Mountain.

Claudius Smith was a leader of the "Cowboys," who took advantage of dissensions among civilians as well as the opposing armies of British and Continentals. Most recent description, and one embodying the more credible of previous tales, is given by Carl Carmer in *The Hudson:*

> The feeling between noncombatants in the valley grew bitterer than it had ever been. Mounted bands of lawless men infested the neutral ground that extended for nearly a score of miles between the upriver Continentals and the downriver British. Claudius Smith, the "Cowboy of the Ramapos," who claimed to be a Tory, led one such group of outlaws. They made swift raids on the river farms, stealing cattle and livestock, which they sold in Manhattan. Sometimes an unlucky wagon train of supplies for Washington's army, too weakly guarded to withstand the attack of Smith's

wild horsemen, would disappear mysteriously and completely. There were tales of the torture of old men and women in the effort to make them give up their savings, of sudden descents on little outlying communities and the murder of helpless inhabitants. Occasionally the Cowboys clashed with an equally dastardly gang of cut-throats called the Skinners who claimed to favor the Revolutionary party, but never troubled to ask the political beliefs of the farmers from whom they stole. Tory and Revolutionary farmers alike heaved sighs of relief whenever these murderous bully-boys succeeded in destroying each other.

For his sins, Claudius Smith danced at the end of a rope in his stocking feet, before the war was over. He took his shoes off just before he swung to prove that his mother had not told the truth. She had said he would die with his boots on. Just to make him an ironic post-humorous prop to law and order, the builders of the courthouse at Goshen, west of the Hudson, used his skull as a brick over the doorway.

The Claudius Smith's Caves are two horizontal cracks at the foot of successive cliffs, the upper crack being some 8 to 10 feet wide and 30 feet long, with a depth of 6 to 8 feet, the lower crevice longer and deeper, but not quite so high of ceiling. Either one is large enough to shelter quite a large party and they are often visited and used as a refuge in time of storm.

And the ever sleepy George Washington, at one time, on a hot summer day, following a foray upon the bandits, is declared to have slept in a cave near his headquarters in Newburgh! This is no more legendary than some of the many houses in which he is reputed to have slumbered half his life away around the country, but no one seems able to point out the exact hole to be able to say, "George Washington slept here."

Even O. Henry missed some of the romance and mystery of his Bagdad on the Subway, but modern writers are digging some of it up. Through his keyhole, Walter Winchell has found secret passages in some of the old buildings on the Bowery which he says were once used as hideouts for criminals, and others in Wall Street which were hangouts for pirates in the seventeenth century; and it is no secret that one can walk for miles in the many underground passages that have been bored beneath Manhattan's topheavy structures. Rockefeller Center has block after block of such subway tunnels, leading from one building to the other, with a different sort of surprise at every turn in the many shops and shoppes that line the passages.

It is possible to travel from one country to another in these passages, for they lead, for instance, from the British Empire building to La Maison Française and ramble around from other foreign country edifices to give one an international spelunking trip in brilliantly lighted ways.

Times Square is a maze comparable to Carlsbad Caverns in its twists and turns, as many a bewildered stranger has discovered in trying to get to the right train; and when it comes to Brooklyn, abandon all hope without a guide at some of the three-decker caverns through which the trains roar.

More secret than these public passages is one which is attached to a historic building, the Old Merchant's House at 29 East Fourth Street, which has been taken over by the Historic Landmarks Society. This house was built for Joseph Brewster, a New York merchant, and sold to Seabury Tredwell, another man of trade, when Andrew Jackson was President, in the 1830's.

This is a place of wide, hollow partitions, trapdoors hidden under closet drawers and leading down a ladder, in one instance, to a dungeon-like chamber below—and if you can find a dependable Oriental guide to Chinatown's underworld, you might discover hundreds of secret places under the buildings and even running beneath streets from one den to another. Tarrytown has its Philipse Castle, with a secret passage leading from a bedroom to a garret, and only to be entered by turning the right peg among several in the back of a closet.

Other cities and towns have their underworlds, as well, but New York certainly has more miles of rock-walled caverns made by man than any other city in America, if not more than London and Paris, and this does not include sewers; we will not go into those.

Of quite different character and usage, but appropriately considered in this chapter, are the somewhat obscure but certainly historical Hough's Caves—which appear to be one cave with two openings—close beside the road between Martinsburg and Lowville in Lewis County. Reputed to have a "travelable" distance of 500 feet between the two entrances, Hough's Cave was a "station" on the Underground Railroad which transported escaped slaves through the north country of New York to Canada and freedom. Horatio Hough, an estimable gentleman, is said to have been the "station master" who hid the fugitive blacks in this cavern.

Horatio Hough was the father of Dr. Franklin B. Hough, historian and "Father of American Forestry," who wrote some seventy-eight volumes, many of them histories of the northern counties of New York, one of which is a *History of Lewis County,* originally published in 1860 and brought out in a new and enlarged edition in the 1880's. Nowhere, in either volume, does Franklin B. Hough refer to the caves or their supposed usages. But in a small and more modern history used in the schools, and in the still more modern *New York State Guide,* compiled by the Federal Writers' Project, such references are found.

The exact quotation from *An Elementary History of the State of New York,* by Harry F. Landon, published in Watertown, 1932, is as follows:

> Two or three lines of the Underground Railroad came up through northern New York. One went into Canada near Malone, another is supposed to have entered Canada in the Thousand Island region. Escaped slaves are believed to have been hidden in Hough's Caves near Lowville.

The Guide makes it more positive, and old residents of Martinsburg and Lowville say that it is certain that Horatio Hough did make such humanitarian use of the cave.

This appears to be the only instance in all of New York State or of New England, for that matter, where an underground area was actually used as a station on this maze of "lines." There were several crossing lines, such as a connection between Troy and Bennington, Vermont, and between northern Massachusetts towns and Brattleboro, Vermont, and at least one steamship line that served as a link, on Lake Champlain.

"Fugitives at Bennington came from Albany by way of Troy and Hoosick," writes Wilber H. Shebert, in his book, *Vermont's Anti-Slavery and Underground Railroad Record,* published at Columbus, Ohio, 1937. He also states that one other crossing place between the two states was "where the Battenkill River crosses the western boundary of the State (of Vermont)."

Evidently Horatio Hough's station was on one of the lines that led toward the Thousand Islands or Malone areas.

Incidentally, Hough got a mountain named after him as well as a cave, the central peak of the Dix Range. Since the traffic in escaped slaves was at its height in the years just preceding the Civil War, and Franklin Hough's history was published just as that war began, it is not strange that he made no mention of this subterranean station, if he knew of it, so that the secret would not be revealed.

The rebellious Anti-Renters doubtless were considered bandits by the Patroons and their subservient law officers, just as Tories were so considered in the Revolution. Quoting one of the leaders of the Anti-Rent Rebellion, sometimes called the Helderberg Rebellion, Carl Carmer in *The Hudson* gives an inkling of the use of caves by these desperate people.

> Down with the Rent! . . . Do not pay them (the patroons). When the Sheriff comes to take your farms, the Natives will *come out from the rocky glens and caves in the mountains* and drive them off. They will come at night and return at night and no one will know whence they came and where they went. . . .

And no one does seem to know, to this day, where they went if they did hide or muster themselves into calico-clad bands, in the caverns in the mountains.

There is a hermit's hole at Niagara Falls, close by the thundering waters of Horseshoe Falls. Charles Hill made this small hole his haven during the depression, to save rent, and he chose a cliff cave so near to the cataract that spray sometimes drifted into his quarters. His reveille in the morning was that roaring thunder and his lullably at night the same. An old-time lumberjack and riverman, Hill did not mind the noise, and he had one of the most magnificent views a man could wish for, looking across to the American Falls and down the great gorge, from the "front porch" of his rock shelter, halfway down the precipice from the top. Here he lived amid a litter of pots, pans and debris, keeping his groceries in an orange crate and boiling up his grub over a crude fireplace. When he clambered up to go to market at Niagara Falls, Ontario—for this cave is on the Canadian side—he left his fox terrier, Tiny, to guard his chosen home. He lived here for three years or more, paying no rent, and declared that his rock haven was warmer than most houses and that he never got really cold. He made a living at odd jobs.

He had a ringside seat at the spectacle of the Falls, winter and summer, and as well of the various daredevil stunts put on by men going over the brink in barrels and big rubber balls. He helped his cousin, "Red" Hill, salvage several bodies of ill-fated men who were banged to death or drowned, in their silly stunts. Known as "Sheep" Hill because he once handled mutton in a butcher shop, Hill's saga came to an end when war brought him bigger and better wages than he ever had made, but his cavern is still there; and, although the famous Cave of the Winds, beneath the Falls, where so many used to go in slickers and boots, is closed, that is still there, too. Rockfalls had made it dangerous, however, and the thrill of being actually beneath that great outpouring torrent is no longer to be enjoyed. The trip was still being advertised in 1946, but the board walk along the base of the Falls that lead to the caves was knocked off several feet from the base. One accident, several years ago, prompted the closing of this unique spelunking opportunity.

If Long Island has any caves at all, they appear to have been man-made, or to be just a few wave-washed or sea-caves along its more exposed coastline.

Curiously, the man-made caves, so far as known, were dug in the search for hidden treasure, and this happened more than a century and a half ago, or even earlier. It is revealed in *The Natural History of New York State,* by W. W. Mather and others, published in 1842 as the first geological report on the Empire State:

> Excavations are found on the east side of many boulders and blocks scattered about on the west side of Ford Pond and Fort Pond Bay. I learned afterwards that these excavations had been made, like those at Kidd's Rock Point and other places on Long Island and along the Hudson River, by credulous persons hunting for the money reported to have been buried by the noted pirate, Captain Kidd, who is said to have killed all the sailors he had employed to bury the money, as soon as the work was done. Singular ceremonies were performed by these persons to keep the devil away during their search!!!

Kidd's Rock and Kidd's Rock Point on the northwest coast of West Hempstead, Long Island, had in the 1840's been wasted away by the sea, Mather reports, after resisting it for unknown centuries.

The author being a human fly in Railroad Cave, Austin's Glen, Catskill

The unique "keyhole" passage in Knox Cave

## *Chapter XV*

# THE CATSKILL MANLIUS

Dr. George H. Chadwick, geologist, historian and somewhat of a speleologist, who lives in a hill-top house two miles west of Catskill, as the crow flies—and a crow can get up there more easily than a man—has located some sixteen caves in the Catskill Quadrangle. This is an area in Greene, Columbia, Ulster and Dutchess Counties, mapped by the United States Geological Survey in its most recent program, 1941, and containing about 270 square miles of mountainous country—and this is real cave country. Much of it is underlaid or outcropped with Manlius limestone, that dull gray, softish rock which goes mostly into the manufacture of cement.

There is one cave which, as you read this, may be part of a state highway or some building that you enter, for the quarrymen of the North American Cement Company dug it out of the very top of a rock hill, in toto, in autumn, 1946, with a steam shovel and the use of much dynamite. Incident to this destruction many interesting specimens of fossils and cave formations were revealed and carried away, some of them to add to the collections of minerals and other natural curiosities in the Mower Memorial Museum or Science Center which Dr. Chadwick has promoted and the Natural Science Association of the Catskills is sponsoring.

This cave, or a small part of it, was known as Bear's Den, before the quarrying began. It was a small opening in the base of an abrupt outcrop of Manlius limestone that towers right above U. S. Highway 9W, just south of the little settlement of Alsen, a little over four miles south of Catskill.

The quarry itself is known as the Manlius Quarry or North Quarry, the character of the rock rather poor grade and having to be mixed with a better grade to make cement, but so easy to get at and transport that its operation has been profitable.

Carl Courson, of Mount Marion, an employee of the company, a keen student of nature and especially of geology, kindly took me on a special visit to this quarry cave on a mild December morning. Stopping at a bridge where a small stream trickles out from crevices in a sheer gray cliff, on the east side of the road, the crevices apparently part of some sort of a cave, or at least of the intricate and extensive underground drainage system that the Catskill Quadrangle has, we stumbled upon a large and very dead eel. It must have perished from the cold as it climbed up from far below, out of an arm of the Hudson River known as Duck Cove. This was a specimen that we did not care to add to our collection, preferring only to speculate upon the mysteries of the overland travels of these strange creatures of the seas. The trickle of water out of the sheer cliff may be from a curious phenomenon that we later visited known as The *Straeke* (pronounced "Streaky," and being Dutch for The Strip) or more probably from The Great Vly, a swamp directly west of the outpour, although varying altitudes make it doubtful. At any rate, here we had found Eel Cave.

In the Manlius Quarry we clambered over a man-made talus of broken rock, before which stood a silent steam shovel, for it was Sunday, Courson led the way to where a rope dangled, one he had thoughtfully fastened to a projection from the roof of the remainder of the vanishing cavern, and which was of great aid in getting into the yawning hole in the very summit of the rock hill.

The entrance gave great promise, but the promise was not kept, for the tunnel that ran due north was small, low-roofed, a belly-crawl passage, perhaps 50 feet in its total traversable extent. I had been advised that this cave presented a geological problem that I might help to solve. Little as I felt qualified to solve any geological problem, it happened that by the comparison of other similar hill-top caves I was able to agree with Dr. Chadwick's theory that this hill was once a low place which the glaciers had planed down to, aeons ago, and their irresistible plowing and the flow of melting ice from them had packed a part of the cavern tightly with clay and left sufficient water flowing through to manufacture formations, such as stalactites and stalagmites.

The steam shovel and blasting had cut away one-half of the plugged part of the winding tunnel of the cave, which ran in a semi-circle through the rock hill, and we had a profile view of these clay packs from the quarry top. There was damp clay and sand on the cave floor and, lo and behold, quantities of stalactites and a few stalagmites, loosened by the blasting, of which we scooped up all we could conveniently drag out, crawling.

My plunder included several miniature candelabras, small stalactites formed in rows, all of them hollow and about the size of a clay dudeen pipestem, some larger, all very white. Carl lugged out a stalagmite, base and all, weighing some fifteen pounds, and later shouldered it and toted it up the half-mile steep to the Science Center for the museum collection.

A parting look at the quarry and the cave gave me a twinge of regret that modern search for building materials must erase this prehistoric rock shelter which may once have harbored bears for their winter slumber, but the discovery of specimens of rather rare sort helped smother our regret. Mr. Courson had found a beautiful quartz crystal here, for instance, with thin layers of clay looking like gold leaf in it, one of those glassy things that are cherished by mineralogists everywhere.

The Streake or Streake Lake Sink, but a few rods away, was as dry as an upland meadow, this day, a long swale between low hills grown to coarse marsh grass as thick as hair. In rainy seasons the basin fills up to a depth of a dozen feet or more with water. A tiny brook rambles through the basin, becoming a sizable freshet from the watershed surrounding the Streake, probably named as a natural landmark for boundary identification between properties. A transmission line with tall steel towers runs close to the east shore of the Streake, and close to the foot of the middle one of three that border the basin is a small hole, no larger than a dishpan, which is the only visible outlet, but through which the waters empty, flowing underground into the Hudson. This is the Catskill replica of No Bottom Pond of Austerlitz. No caves, however.

Austin's Glen is quite another thing, a rare place indeed. Through the glen, and alongside a cliff, rising high above the wide, rambling Catskill, near where the Kaaterskill joins, runs the ancient, abandoned grade of the Canajoharie & Catskill Railroad. Here are three caves, perhaps one or two more that cannot be, or have not been, opened for exploration.

Entrance to Austin's Glen is through the grounds of a sturdy Manlius limestone house erected by early members of the Austin family and still owned by descendants. It stands on the south side of N. Y. 23-145, near a roadside marker which says:

Paper Mill, First in Greene County, 1/4 mile at foot of hill.
Built in 1800 by Nathan Benjamin.

You can't miss it, for Austin's Glen is directly back of the stone house, and a trail leads down, down into it, onto the old railroad grade, a relic of the bitter battle of the Erie Canal, when the up-and-alive citizens of Catskill attempted to have the canal routed to their town instead of to Albany. Failing in this, they built the railroad to try to divert the freight which the canal would take away from them, for Catskill—which boasts of being so old that it is the home of Uncle Sam—had been an important traffic center because of the ancient King's Road from New York City, and the Susquehanna Turnpike. But the Canajoharie & Catskill narrow-guage, with the sharpest curve of any railroad in the country, so sharp that the engineer and caboose conductor exchanged tobacco as the train curled about a 150-degree arc, failed to get the freight after all. The grade was adapted to serve the famous old Mountain House, with a cog-railway extension to this hotel, and was renamed the Catskill Mountain Railroad.[1]

[1] Histories of Green County relate that before the Erie Canal was completed, the county seat, Catskill, commanded the trade of adjacent counties west, and of

Naturally, the cave that is within a man's stride of the old grade is known as Railroad Cave. Its entrance is an abrupt well, 20 feet deep, a slit in the rock just wide enough to admit a man, sidewise, and so sheer of sides that a rope is necessary for descent and ascent save for the most agile rock climbers.

At the foot of the slit, tunnels run two ways, a total distance of some 200 feet, with pools of water, banks of soft sandy mud, very few small formations—but one of the tunnels runs down to the edge of the Catskill, right beneath the old railroad, and this would make a better entrance and exit, save that some foolish persons have plugged it up with railroad ties and rocks.

Lizard's Cave, a companion to this one, opens a bit up the cliff, an unassuming, choked entrance filled with leaves, sticks and earth washed in, requiring the use of a garden hoe to clear the way for a sliding descent on a gentle slope, into a low chamber. Here a sharp turn to the left leads to a well 15 feet deep, slightly wider than the Railroad Cave slit, with convenient ridges for toe-holds, and a curious natural keyhole at one edge to which a rope can be tied for safer negotiation.

At the bottom of this well, which is paved with soft sand and a bit of gravel, there seemed to be no more to Lizard's Cave, but again the hoe came into play, and with the aid of that tool and a battered old basin and a broken shovel left inside, enough of the packed earth was pulled from beneath a narrow arch of rock so that entrance was possible—by lying flat on one's back, and heeling in, headfirst, shoving sand away with the back of

the south tier, through to Lake Erie and a portion of Pennsylvania. It was a large wheat market and had the most extensive flouring mills in the state. Later, about 1817, many tanneries flourished, using hemlock bark from the nearby woods.

The Canajoharie & Catskill Railroad was incorporated in 1831 but was not built until 1838 or '39. It had one undependable locomotive which had to be taken for repairs to Paterson, New Jersey, by steamer and horse-drawn vehicles, more than once, and it finally failed and, "a stage horse replaced it."

The track was of wooden stringers plated with iron straps. It was finally dismantled, and the iron salvaged, but in 1882 a narrow-gauge road was built on the old roadbed from Catskill to South Cairo. The grade was a terror. The road rose from 13 feet altitude to 555 feet, and one grade rose 78 feet in a mile.

the head and collecting considerable in the hair and pockets and pants.

Mr. Frank Solari, of New York City, a veteran spelunker who has explored many caves in the British Isles, his native land, and quite a few in this country, heeled himself through headfirst, upside down, and began to yell with wonder, thereby tempting three more of us to wiggle through.

The caveman's cry of, *"Oh, Oh, OH!"* is seldom from fright or danger but from uncontrollable wonder at what his eyes take in as he flashes his light about.

Beyond that low archway was a high chamber, its walls glistening with drops of water impregnated with calcite minerals, its roof painted white with snowlike rockflow—and beyond that another, longer, loftier chamber with grottoes and adits of even greater beauty, and still another, really a part of the second one but barred by so narrow a "lemon squeezer" that some rock climbing was necessary to get up to a wider passage. The roof, here, was at least 35 feet above the floor, arching and opening into pretty grottoes, one of them showing the dangling roots of trees, small tendrils that had crept down in through crevices from the rocky ground above, for the cavern rises close to the surface at one end.

There were no lizards here, but perhaps the cave was named because of that low-arch gateway through which, at times, only a lizard or a snake might crawl, for evidences were plenty that flowing water completely blocks it with sand, and the broken shovel and basin testified that others had dug their way in. Dr. Chadwick had explored this and Railroad Cave last in 1912; he now saves his strength for the half-mile climb to his chosen roost, the former Alan Ireland mansion. We walked past the ruins of Dr. Chadwick's birthplace, a once fine house built on the side of the cliff, with a great wall of limestone blocks forming a terrace support, close to the old railroad line. No wonder he knew these caves and brought along a hoe!

There is still a third cave in Austin's Glen, and this is called Austin's Cave, though it is not so interesting as the other two.

It opens, with a big yawn, near the very top of the cliff, and is best reached from a point opposite the Salisbury Hotel, a summer hostelry of Civil War architectural type on N. Y. 23. A faint trail leads through a thin patch of sumach, poplars, and cherry trees to a fine lookout on the edge of the cliff, overlooking the wide, rock-bottomed Catskill, and giving a view of the natural rock base of the old dam which once furnished power for Nathan Benjamin's paper mill. Across the stream rises the sheer, fir-clad slope of Jefferson Heights, and up there you can see the Rip Van Winkle Bridge, just two miles away, to the east.

Such is the lure of Catskill Manlius cave country, and with time—several days, if not weeks—to explore here, there might be found a dozen more caves of sorts. One that was formerly an extensively traveled cavern is the Cauterskill or Packer's Cave, opening off a gully up a small run that empties into the Kaaterskill, near Baer's Camps, which are at a bridge over this stream where the Rip Van Winkle Trail crosses. A rockfall inside has shut off much of this cavern, and we rock climbers had had enough for one day. Dusk was falling, and it was time to return to the caveman's center at the Saulpaugh Hotel to wash off mud, shake out sand, and eat enormously. After all, four caves in one day, plus the rock and mountain climbing that goes with it, should satisfy the most eager spelunker.

If you go to Austin's Cave, do not even try to get down in the wells. They are deep, dangerous, and lead nowhere—and do not even try to reach the beautiful formations in a narrow grotto at the extreme end of the first, short passage. They are unreachable, thank you. Just look. And do not call the Catskill or the Katterskill, or any of the "kills," creeks or rivers, because "kill" means a stream, and the map-makers are redundant when they print them as "Catskill Creek," etc.

Catskill means "wildcat creek," and Katterskill means the same thing, in the original Dutch. And do not go looking for Rip Van Winkle's Cave, for there isn't any; that durable old rip slept for twenty years right out in the open beside the bowling alleys. Come rain, come snow, come hail, come burning sun,

Rip must have his sleep and after that a toddy at the tavern, and "we won't count this one."[2]

For other caves in the Catskills, see Dr. Chadwick and get a Quadrangle map. Visit the Mower Memorial Museum, that elaborate house built by the author, Ireland, as a retreat, without benefit of any water save what fell from the skies, requiring an extensive roof drainage system to catch rain, a cistern, and a trip down the half-mile steep for water to drink—or other liquids.

Here are some caves that Dr. Chadwick lists and locates on the map: Quarry Hill Cave or Moon's Cave; Cave or Tunnel between Alsen and West Camp close to 9W; Natural Stone Bridge over a tiny stream just west of the Old King's Road in Saugerties; Indian Caves beside Esopus Creek about a mile east of Mount Marion; three caves north of Alsen, near 9W, just west of Duck's Cove on the Hudson; Haner's Cave and an underground stream along the Rip Van Winkle Trail, three-quarters of a mile due west of 9W and one and one-half miles east of Pine Grove school, right on the trail; and a cave in Saugerties, which is or used to be much visited by the children of the town. Dr. Chadwick calls our Eel Cave a Blind Cave. There are plenty of those everywhere, a temptation to start pulling rocks out of a vanishing trickle of water to see whether a spelunker can pour himself into the unknown.

It is getting a little off the cave trail here, but not far, to mention something about the old Catskill Mountain House and its "million dollar view," as it was recorded by swarms of visitors, among whom were many notables, who really raved in almost lurid language about it. Some keen press agent collected the ravings of over a dozen of these persons, and incorporated them in an advertising brochure for The Mountain House which sprawled out atop Pine Orchard Mountain at an altitude of 3,000 feet above the sea.

The brochure, a copy of which came to hand in the Ballard

[2]Irving wrote that Rip fell asleep in a hollowed-out rock, which by no stretch of imagination can be considered a cave.

Historical Library at the Berkshire Atheneum in Pittsfield, Massachusetts, is titled:

The Scenery of
The Catskill Mountains
as Described by
Irving, Cooper, Bryant, William Gaylord Clark,
N. P. Willis, Harriet Martineau, Tyrone Power,
Park Benjamin, Thomas Cole and other eminent writers.

The booklet was priced at twelve and one-half cents.

Among other claims to the fame of the long look from the summit of Pine Orchard, was Miss Martineau's sober declaration that she could see the Atlantic Ocean from here, and one of the galaxy of writers declared that it was the one view in the world that Queen Victoria of England wished to see.

But even up here on the heights, or just below them, we are not entirely off the cave trail, for there are the Katterskill Falls and Haines Falls, the former leaping off a ledge of the Clove, beneath Sunset Rock, dropping like a rainspout stream, veiling behind its spraying cloud of water some tiny shelf caves, and forming ice caves in winter that reluctantly melt until May.

Of these falls and others Dr. Chadwick lately made a study from the geological standpoint, for there has been much argument among geologists as to whether local glaciers may have existed in this latitude after the melting of the ice cap from off this region. The good man wrote to a friend in April, 1946:

> In the vicinity of Prattsville, Dr. John L. Rich, a Catskill Mountain boy, discovered, years ago, a convincing case of such lingering icework and published his find, but it was met with unresponsiveness on the part of the glaciologists. One day, being near, I thought I would run over and look. To my surprise it was totally convincing. Later I got Prof. Fairchild to look at it with me and he also was satisfied. In 1940 a dozen car loads of our New York State Geological Association followed me there and agreed it was a place well worth seeing.

While hundreds of thousands of persons have swarmed into the Catskills and climbed to their summits to see the views, probably not two dozen have sought the scenic underground, and that is where we have been poking our heads in, for a look at the wonders that so few have ever seen.

Slide Mountain, the highest peak in the Catskills, rising 4,200 feet above sea level, has been described by many a breathless climber, including John Burroughs, the famous naturalist, who visited it often—and to whom is dedicated a tiny rock-shelter cave at an altitude of about 4,000 feet. The shelter is a hollow beneath rugged cliff projections, suitable for refuge from rain and snow—if anyone is rugged enough to climb it in winter. Some of the "Cloud Splitters" of the Adirondack Mountain Club have done so, and it is the goal of all of these who reach for the clouds. The cave has been somewhat man-made, by piling flat rocks to form a low wall in front of it and laying evergreen boughs across the "front porch." There is a tablet above it, inscribed to Burroughs.

Curiously, Burroughs mentions it only casually in his writings, although he described the rocks of the summit in some detail, as well as its scenery and birds, especially a thrush, called Bicknell's thrush, that he says is unique to this mountain, but which later was discovered to be "a somewhat more southern form of the gray-cheeked thrush, and is found on the higher mountains of New York and New England."

Of the rocks, Burroughs says they are a kind of conglomerate or "pudden stone," which consists of "cemented quartz pebbles that underlie the coal measures."

It may be that Burroughs was referring to this cave in his book, *Riverby,* when he tells of finding "an ice-cave . . . vast masses of ice with crystal pools of water near." Water was what he and his companions were hunting for after their climb.

It was the proud accomplishment of Miss Elizabeth Little, of Menands, a veteran member of the Albany Chapter, Adirondack Mountain Club, to make Slide Mountain her forty-eighth peak over 4,000 feet high, one summer day recently, and to stop for a salute at Burrough's Cave, which appears to be the highest in New York State and the most "literary."

The Catskills are full of clefts in mountain walls, called Cloves. Near Woodstock is a typical one called the Plattekill Clove, and according to T. Morris Longstreth, who has written a sort of New York State mountain series, the local inhabitants call a gorge at the top of the Clove the Grand Canyon of the Catskills, and at the very tip-top is a sort of cave known as the Devil's Kitchen; but how such a satanic cookery happens to be located in The Wall of Manitou is an anomaly, indeed.

Near Katterskill, Longstreth found a "lemon squeezer" sort of a cavelet with fancifully named natural features, such as the Druid Rocks, Elfin Pass, and Fairy Spring. In climbing Peekamoose, from Ashokan, he also found a Blue Hole through which flows the waters of Rondout Creek, "the clearest of all waters," and described it as a place where "if ever Pan comes to America he will love the Blue Hole most of all, and its rocky ledges crowned with the fine-textured beeches are the place for him to sit and make his music in."

It is to such mountain climbers, many of them, that the spelunker owes the discovery of many a cave and cavelet which would otherwise go unknown and unnamed. Far down near the New Jersey line, at Port Jervis, on Hawk's Nest, where are the Lifting Rocks, previously described, is Indian Joe's Cave, where this character lived. It is, or was, just west of Tusten Station, now abandoned, save when Boy Scouts come up for the summer camp period. It was mostly destroyed, along with several other Indian Rock Shelters, or just rock shelters, when the Erie Railroad blasted a way through the ledges. Many Indian artifacts have been found in these shelters.

## *Chapter XVI*

# DEEPER IF NOT BETTER HOLES

PROBABLY the deepest cave in New York State is one near Sprakers, known as Mitchell's Cave, but recent visitors agree that it is not a "better 'ole"—such as Old Bill was always seeking in World War I. It has been known for at least a century and a quarter. It was named for the late Professor Samuel L. Mitchell, of New York City, who seems to have been one of the first to make an official exploration of it, in 1821. At any rate his survey of it was published in Horatio Gates Spafford's *Gazeteer* in 1824.

The entrance is in the margin of some woods on Nose Hill, on land owned by the Meehan family, who have fitted up a little picnic ground in the vicinity. It is to be reached from Sprakers by turning south from Route 5-S, and a mile and a half on turning left onto a road that leads to the Meehan property and what is locally called the Palisades of the Mohawk, in the town of Root, Montgomery County.

Estimates of the depth of this cavern vary from 300 to 500 feet, and of the total extent with lateral passages or rooms, some 700 feet. There are said to be ten separate rooms, at constantly descending levels, and two or three other side rooms.

The Mitchell exploring party descended into it by ropes, the first drop being 16 feet to an opening 11 feet by 30 feet and 13 feet high. Then came another passage of about 20 feet to another room, and so on, to the tenth room, "and they supposed they had descended 500 feet," according to an account taken from Beer's *History of Montgomery County,* published in 1878.

But the author of the account, J. R. Simms, remarks:

> Distance, as I know from experience, seems long in such a place; of course they did not go to any such perpendicular depth from the surface.

As Roger Johnson puts it, "A cave mile is just about ten feet." He led a party on an exploration of Mitchell's Cave September 22, 1935, under guidance of Edward J. Sheehan, Montgomery County Archivist, who has kindly furnished a copy of the old account.

Well, Mr. Johnson usually refers to the cave as The Hog Wallow, and from photographs taken of the Yankee party, at the time of their crawl, the allegation appears somewhat appropriate. But in olden times wild predictions were made as to what a natural wonder there was here that could be developed and rival such as Howe's Cave, and imaginative descriptions of the many beautiful formations were published.

One party, led by Martin Carson, with Doctors Red and Antis, and others, visited it in 1837, and Carson's story and those of others were given to Historian Simms in 1853. Seemingly the tale had grown tall with the years, for it told of getting down to the thirteenth room, where they found masses of stalactites and a dome or rotunda and believed they were deep down under the Mohawk River, as they heard water running, but they "met with no water except in little pools or cavities, from which they slaked their thirst."

Another exploration was made by the crew of the "State Scow," which was used on the canal to keep it clear of dangerous obstructions, and also to seek leaks, such as muskrats make.

"The Captain proposed, after an unpleasant duty, to give his hands the afternoon, and with them explore the mooted wonder of the mountain," wrote Simms, "a proposition readily accepted."

There were a dozen in the party, armed with candles and a "globe lamp," and three of them, with the lamp, got down to the brink of what seemed to be a deep and rapid stream which went thundering far below. Here they stopped and returned, and "supposed they had gone down nearly or quite to the bed of the river, a distance of several hundred feet."

They ran into water and mud, and so did the Johnson party, and all agree that it is a deep, dark, and dangerous place in some areas and not very beautiful. The rock is mostly gneiss, according to Simms, and the few stalactites that anyone had collected were of an ashy color, and not nice. Dr. John Laucks, of Schoharie County, who visited it, hoping to get some fine formations, found but a few stalactites, and that is not strange; the strangest thing is that gneiss rock should have any such formations, for they are usually found only in limestone or its varieties such as gypsum or conglomerates.[1]

There was a mystery about a supposed secret tunnel or cave near Lake Mohonk, until the Smileys revealed that a member of the family had dug the hole in a search for minerals, and it had been forgotten. This tunnel was in the side of a mountain and was 500 feet long, with 250 feet of side adits. Just what minerals were being sought does not appear, but probably iron.

Curiously, the date of its "discovery" is several times given as 1848, although Spafford's *Gazeteer* had it in 1824, and said it had been visited in 1821, so there are various discrepancies in various accounts, which somewhat add to the mystery.

Prodigious are the old, abandoned mines at Ellenville, sometimes called Ice Caves, where excavations were made, not only perpendicularly but horizontally, to get at preferred strata of rock. Ice forms over large areas in the mines and remains until late in spring or early summer. The depths are not very tempting, for the rock is treacherous where it has been cracked by blasting. There are many such mine holes scattered about the state, and some that are in the category of lost mines because they have caved in or been overgrown with brush and trees. Few if any have anything to recommend them in the way of beauty, and most are dangerous, although several iron mines may be entered and explored without too much trouble. The hard ore resists breakage, but be wary of the pits which hold, sometimes, deep pools of nasty water.

Roger Johnson refers to Clark's or Van Vliet's Cave in Scho-

[1]Recent photographs in Mitchell's Cave show some splendid glistening rockflow formations which must have been formed from limestone.

harie as a "nasty hole" that he got into in 1936, but sometimes a muddy entrance leads to something wonderful, which is why spelunkers keep on crawling in old clothes even in places which may be called hog wallows.

The Rosendale cement quarries, still worked, are described by Carl Carmer in *The Hudson*. He wrote that "some Ulster County people say you can walk all the way from Rosendale to Kingston through the middle of the earth if you know the way. Others say that it is so cold in one of the caverns that the underground lake which has formed there stays frozen the year round, and midsummer skating parties could be held if the guests could find their way to it."

We offer you Van Bergen's Hole-in-the-Ground as a realistically named cave, at Coxsackie. This is a narrow slit between large rocks, with an outlet in Haswell's Ravine, which is very pretty. Explorers did not find the cave very pretty. It was difficult, wet, and unremarkable as a cavern.

Diana's Well on the Cairo stream is described in *Picturesque Catskills,* by de Lisser, under the heading "Rambles of an Artist," as being "a very curious and odd freak of nature."

This is near Shingle Kill Falls on the creek of that name, one mile south of Cario; "a natural well 5 or 6 feet in diameter, smooth and round, and some 50 feet in depth. It used to be called bottomless, or from 100 to 150 feet deep," and "it has doubtless been much deeper, but is quite filled with loose rocks and sticks and other debris."

Raymond H. Torrey in the *New York Walk Book,* tells of the Brundige Cave on the east side of Brundige Mountain, about a mile north of Burnt Sawmill Bridge, a perpendicular crack 3 or 4 feet in width, and extending upward for 10 or 15 feet, with very small floor space and nothing much else about it save that it is a typical mountain cliff cave.

One of the most remarkable examples of a mountain cave is described by A. T. Shorey. It is at Chimney Mountain and is so deep that a candle lowered on a string went out of sight. The upthrust of the chimney itself is the last remaining Grenville limestone in the region; the rest has been borne away or ground away by glaciers and washed into the streams and lost.

A most careful and detailed geological study of this unique topographic feature is reported in the New York State Museum Bulletin, No. 308, of May 1937, in *Geology of The Thirteenth Lake Quadrangle, New York,* by Medora Hooper Krieger, a student of geology who married a geologist of note, Dr. Philip Krieger, of Columbia University. When he died, she continued her work in the field and laboratory.

Mrs. Krieger's account states that the rift in the upthrust of Chimney Mountain is more than 600 feet long, 150 to 200 feet deep, and 200 to 250 feet wide across the top, with the bottom of the rift and eastern base of Chimney Rock—a precipitous wall rising about 35 feet higher than the general level of the opposing right wall—strewn with angular blocks of rock, up to 20 feet and more across, which have accumulated since the development of the rift. This rift is entirely within the Grenville strata, consisting of gneisses, quartzite and mixed rocks resting upon the granite of the main mass of the mountain.

Dr. William J. Miller previously had studied this formation and offered his theory of how it was formed—that it is Postglacial, the rift lacking any evidences of glaciation and, judging from the trees grown up inside, at least a century old, probably much older.

Mrs. Krieger adds that other rifts and joints appear to have been caused by a "slumping of all the Grenville rocks down the mountain side," and mentions an ice cave, the main one of several, located about 230 feet from the top of the west wall of the rift. She says it can be traced for at least 500 feet and is well developed (open) for at least 200 feet. The bottom is a jumble of rocks and the deepest part "continuously filled with snow."

She compares these crevices and rifts and caves to those in the Shawangunk Mountains, and particularly the Ellenville "ice caves." She also describes two caves discovered in 1931 and 1932, one near the north end and one near the south end of a rift, east of Lake Minnewaska, near Newburgh.

The one at the south end was explored and found to be quite extensive, having several rooms, with icicles hanging from the ceiling in mid-summer. The north cave was measured to a depth of 100 feet by lowering a weighted rope into it. These may well be called Charles Carroll's Caves, for it was he, proprietor of the Chimney Mountain House at Lake Humphrey, King's Flow, who discovered them. They were formed, it is believed, by the movement of rocks downward or the wedging of ice shoving up overhanging layers of rock.

Chimney Mountain is to be reached from Indian Lake Village, which is on Route 28, 42 miles northwest of Lake George Village. It is southeast of Indian Lake Village about eight miles, and reached by a road to the foot of it, or can be reached from Route 10, going south from Indian Lake Village about two miles, with a turn southeast, and continuing to the end of a dirt road. The cavern appears as a curious chimney within a chimney, so to speak. So far as is known no one has ever reached its bottom, perhaps because no one brought along enough rope, and here is a challenge to spelunkers and mountaineers, par excellence.

A great fissure yawns in the side of Dibble Mountain, which was formerly called Miller Mountain because here the Millerites, a religious sect, climbed to wait for the end of the world. It is southeast of Crown Point, and although Dibble Mountain can be easily found and is on the map, the fissure cavern itself is difficult to locate, says Scout Shorey, who has gone on foot over some of the most wild and wooly places in New York State. It can be approached by clambering up from the base of some cliffs or by just "climbing up the other side of Dibble Mountain and down a ways." This is really a Purgatory, in gneiss rock, geologically speaking, great open clefts, then some portions roofed over by fallen slabs and almost totally dark inside. A huge rock that has tumbled down into one of these clefts is called the Devil's Counter, and progress is barred by the devilish thing, over which old Nick is said to have bargained for souls. Beyond this is a deep, dark well which is not tempting to explore, anyway.

The numerous prodigious passes, gorges, and clefts in the mountains in the very heart of the Adirondacks have been explored by very few persons, to this day. Early explorations, as reported in the writings of anonymous individuals in guidebooks, appear to have been made mostly by proxy or the aid of vivid imaginations.

In the wild area known as the Mount Marcy Region to the New York State Conservation Department, and as the Mount Marcy Quadrangle to the surveyors of the United States Geodetic Survey, are some of the more breath-taking rifts in rock mountains, with a litter of jumbled rock caves, amounting to caverns in some cases.

On a June day in 1922, a party of five, one family, arrived in a snowstorm—yes in June—at Cascade Lakes. They were on a motor-camping trip which was to end at the Mississippi River, going by way of Ottawa, Pembroke, Mattawa, North Bay, the Nickel Range, and The Soo—pioneers over the most northerly road that a car could negotiate in Ontario. They did not know then that they were in the heart of cave country of a sort, nor that some of them were much later to become enthusiastic spelunkers.

Cascade Lakes were known at an early time as Edmond's Ponds, and Cascade Mountain, as Long Pond Mountain. The chilled travelers, seeking a place to camp for the night, were at once awed by the prodigious, steep heights around them in this narrow pass, and fearful of freezing that night.

We were taken in by a merciful caretaker at the yet unopened Cascades Lake Club and, even then, despite a roaring wood fire in a box stove in one room, slept, shiveringly, with all our clothes on and our cots heaped with blankets.

# DEEPER IF NOT BETTER HOLES

Without knowing it, for our maps were mostly of Canada, we were surrounded by caverns and gorges and holes in which ice stays all summer. We were not far from Indian Pass, Hunter's Pass, Chapel Pond Pass, and others not even yet named or known.

Indian Pass has been many times described, but it is still difficult to paint its picture in words. It is one of the most wonderfully impressive places of this sort in the country. One of those early, anonymous guidebook writers described it as best he could in *A Descriptive and Historical Guide to the Valley of Lake Champlain and The Adirondacks,* published at Burlington, Vermont, in 1871, by R. S. Styles Steam Printing House.

Indian Pass, the writer said, is "in the impressive aboriginal *Otreyark*"—the Indian name for The Stony Giants, and continues:

> It occupies a narrow ravine, formed by a rapid acclivity of Mt. McIntyre on the one side, rising at an angle of 45 degrees, and on the opposite, by the dark, naked wall of a vertical precipice, towering to an altitude of 800 to 1200 feet from the base and extending more than a mile in length. The base is about 2500 feet above tidewater. This deep and appalling gorge is strewn with and probably occupied for several hundred feet with gigantic fragments hurled into it from the impending cliffs by some potent agency. . . .

Potent indeed. Geologists pronounce such a place as this a Purgatory, caused by an earthquake or earth tremor which split rock mountains open, then clashed them together and smashed the rock into thousands of pieces, some of them huge and, in places, tumbled together so that "accidental caves" were left.

A later account of Indian Pass is furnished by A. T. Shorey, who has gone through it:

> The pass is a jumble of huge boulders, some of them with as many as 300 trees growing on them. There are many grottoes and large holes and rock shelters, all filled with hard blue ice that never melts. I call it the last stand of the Ice Age. Walking into the head of the pass is like entering a refrigerator. It is cold on

the hottest day of summer. The head of the pass is 2800 feet above sea-level; Wallface rises to about 3500 feet. From the high point on the trail, 2800 feet elevation, you look down into a Purgatory and up into Heaven. When the mists are floating through the pass and intermittently blotting out the wall of Wallface, the effect is marvelous.

There is a trail through it now, the trail from Heart Lake, five miles south of N. Y. 85-A, at North Elba, which is five miles south of Lake Placid, and the trail runs five miles from Heart Lake to the head of the pass, between the highest rock walls east of the Rockies (Wallface Mountain) and the west end of the McIntyre Range.

The climb to the head of the pass is a short one but stiff. Going down to the west side is a big drop to Henderson Lake in Sanford Lake Valley. The head of the pass is on the great divide between the Hudson and St. Lawrence Rivers, right on the very top of our eastern world, unless one climbs old Mount Marcy, the Indian name *Tahawus,* or Cloud Splitter, as many an Adirondack Mountain Club member has done to get nearer to the clouds and Heaven, at about 50 feet under 5,000 feet altitude.

Hunter's Pass in North Hudson cuts between the precipices of Mount Dix and Nippletop, which are among the highest and most sequestered mountains of the Adirondacks. The pass was named, not for Nimrods chasing game, but for a lumber-camp boss whose headquarters were in the big bowl south of the pass. The lumberjacks came mostly from the Keene Valley, and their route to and from the camp was through this rough and rugged gorge which has "bears' dens" galore in its jumbled rock bottom, and a possible cave atop Nippletop, reported by Walter Collins O'Kane in his *Guide to Adirondack Peaks,* one of those that was "heard about but never found." Today, trails run through it, joining a quarter-mile below the summit of Mount Dix.

There may be a mine of jewels high up on a precipice above the Cascade Lakes. The same old guidebook of 1871 whets the appetite of the treasure seeker with a glowing passage telling of:

> . . . a series of caves which are the deposits of varied gems and minerals and in beauty and variety of material almost rival the story of eastern caverns. Here is found calcerous spar of various colors and crystals of epidots, cocoline and hornblende. The scientific explorer would enjoy in this locality a rich and delightful field.

This sounds much like the salvaged Sterlingbush Crystal Cave that is now, in part, in the State Museum at Albany, but it is not the same, for that deposit was miles away, in the Lowville region, and an experienced trailer and spelunker who helped build the trails through this country says that he knows of no such caves or deposits. All the same, scientific explorers may soon be burrowing into the rocks in search of these reputed jewels and gems. The New York State Museum is interested.

The 1871 guidebook gives a breathless description of the Natural Stone Bridge at Pottersville, which is also described as it now is, in another chapter in this book. The earlier account states:

> The explorer enters a lofty arch, several feet below the surface, carved out by the hand of nature . . . presenting at some points the appearance of almost an exact Gothic structure, and from other views, of broken aisles and abrupt canopies. This dark and gloomy cavern extends a number of rods and is from four to ten feet in width and ten to fifteen feet high. It is the flume way of a large stream which propels a mill and rushes and foams along the rocky descent. . . .

This was before the log jam had plugged the passage through the "lofty arch."

Of gorges well known, and which need little description, there is famous and awesome Ausable Chasm, a river-carved gorge in sandstone that has attracted hundreds of thousands to gaze down into the roaring depths or to take the thrilling boat ride. There is a cave of sorts in the chasm, called the Devil's Oven, a deep, cavernous recess in the rock of one steep bank, and there are those who think that this mighty downpouring through the rock beats all the gorges and chasms in the state.

It is undoubtedly the greatest single tourist attraction in the Adirondack State Park.

On the other hand, the many wild and unspoiled gorges in the northern mountains remain for those who get off the main-traveled routes and toil up and down the foot-trails, or break their own trails to such wonders as Whetstone Pass or Gulf on the east side of Tug Hill Plateau near Lowville. For that matter all the streams that run down off the Adirondack Plateau have beautiful gorges and some caves not even named.

It would never do to omit historic Watkin's Glen, on Seneca Lake, Schuyler County, which the state has exploited for years as a tourist haven—to the detriment of its natural beauties in the judgment of even some of the officials, for it is crowded with all the trimmings of a tourist camp and bathing beach, and only far up in its darker recesses, unspoiled.

The glowing accounts of it published by the Conservation Department in its literature feature it fulsomely as the oldest and best known of the State Parks in the Finger Lakes region, and say "it has long been classed with Niagara Falls, Mammoth Cave and the Natural Bridge of Virginia as one of the scenic wonders of America," but the bedizened old dame isn't what she used to be when the Leatherstockings of the Empire State were roaming the wilds among the Seven Nations. If you can shut your eyes to hot-dog stands and forget that there are 566 steps in one trail and 632 in another at the top of the glen and avoid at night the flood lights that make it an inland Coney Island, it is still beautiful and has some interesting rock formations, cavelets, and potholes.

To get the true picture of the Glen in its pristine beauty one needs to read old guidebooks and ancient historical accounts, which are many, for it has been described by hundreds of writers since it was discovered, and especially since its grand opening to the public, in 1863, and again when it became a State Park in 1906. That great American traveler, "Porte Crayon," once painted a glowing word picture of it in *Harper's Magazine* in a famous series of American travelogs that he wrote.

The greatest cave country of western York State is included in another triangle similar to the eastern cave triangle of land, but much smaller. This tract of limestone extends from the vicinity of Lowville on the southeast, up through Watertown, along the Black River almost to its mouth on Lake Ontario, and then northwesterly almost to Cape Vincent at the source of the St. Lawrence. It extends on the north to the vicinity of Pamelia and includes the localities of Brownville, Limerick and Glen Park.

These caves have been known for over a century. Historian Franklin Hough described the Watertown area caves in his *History of Jefferson County* in the 1840's as being in Black River limestone and Isle la Motte marble and Trenton limestone, "a well-defined mass of greyish blue limestone not exceeding ten feet in thickness," with many fossils to be found in it.

Watertown has two large caves that "blow hot and cold." One was anciently known as Ice Cave and later as Beer Cave. The other, which appears to have no name, is warmer than the average cave, going into the 60's in temperature.

Ice Cave is on the south bank of Black River approximately in the rear of the city hall, near a large gasoline storage plant. The entrance is an opening at the base of a cliff, quite low and near the river's edge. In this cave, says Hough, "the seasons are reversed," for the ice starts forming in spring, and builds up until fall, when it starts to melt, a phenomenon due to the gradual penetration of frost during the winter and the subsequent warming up of the exterior rocks, toward fall. It blows its cold breath out in a fog at times, and Hough says that when he explored it with the outside temperature at 92 in the shade, it was only 32 in the inside.

Ice Cave was discovered in 1838 and was much visited, is supposed to have been used, with others, as a hideout for Indians and British spies, but must have been quite uncomfortable if they used it. It was used at one time as a storage vault for barrels of beer from a nearby brewery.

Judge Crandall F. Phillips, of Watertown, is the present-day authority on the caves of the city and vicinity, having personally explored most of them, and he remembers when a house or shed was erected over the entrance to Ice Cave—when it was called Beer Cave—and recorded the temperature as "approximately 40 degrees the year round." The cave could be followed for several hundred feet in a circuitous route and gave the impression of being formed like a string of beads, the successive chambers being oval or round in shape with a string of passages between. Ice stalactites form in it in summer so as to make passage almost impossible, but it now has no other formations and no sign of life. A few years ago the opening was boarded up by the city because two boys had got trapped and lost inside. Judge Phillips' party, on an exploring visit, divided near the entrance, leaving a candle burning there, and starting to unwind a ball of string. The party that Judge Phillips led wandered away to a distance estimated at some 1,000 feet and suddenly, to their surprise, heard the other party talking close beneath them. They had returned by an upper level to a point right above where they started from, and had the others toss up the ball of string to prove it.

There is an Altar Rock in Ice Cave where couples used to be married during an epidemic of such stunts in the 1880's. The rock is shaped somewhat like a long, high table. A historical novel titled, *The Trail of the Grand Seigneur,* by Olin Linus Lyman, refers to the Watertown caves and weaves some romance about them.[2] Ice or Beer Cave blows its cold air out, while the other large cave in the city, which is on the north side of

[2]This novel, written in the first person, closely resembles some of Cooper's Leatherstocking tales in its style and adventures. The hero, surprising a spy in the woods near Watertown, during the War of 1812, is bested in a hand-to-hand wrestling match, and the spy flees on horseback. He is pursued by the hero and a friend for some miles and "Deadeye" Godfrey, a sharpshooter with a pistol knocks down the spy's horse, firing while at full gallop, and grounds the fugitive—but when our hero makes a dash for him, "in a wild wooded glen bordering the (Kahumahgo) river," the nimble spy vanishes into the earth. The hero had heard of a cave being here and now he plunges boldly into the dark depths with no light to aid him and grapples again with the spy. He manages to hurl him to the

the Black River, near the plant of the Northern New York Utilities and at the north end of Mill Street bridge, draws its breath in. Up until about 1942 there was an opening in the cliff on the river bank whereby one could crawl some 75 feet through a tunnel, approximately 3 feet in diameter, into the cave chambers, fairly large and roomy ones, composed of water-worn rock, and separated by thin stone partitions that have been eroded through to form window-like openings. Judge Phillips estimates that the cave extends in a northerly direction from the river bank about 1,200 feet and is in many places so high that one can walk upright. Some of the rooms are from 20 to 25 feet high, or were until filled with debris of broken rock. There is some flowstone and a milky white concretion at the juncture of ceilings and walls, formed by dripping water, but not stalactitic. There used to be stalactites galore, but only one small room, too tiny to enter, still retains them, together with some stalagmites; there they could not be reached by human hands, which had carried off all the rest.

On the floor of this cave are formations resembling thin white dishes filled with water, very delicate and beautiful.

At Glen Park, down the river, is a third sizeable cave which used to be lighted, and parties were guided through it and sometimes given a boat ride of about 1,000 feet on an underground stream. Hough describes this as it was a century or more ago, saying that it was discovered in 1822 and almost immediately commercialized.

In those early years this Glen Park Cave was beautifully adorned with curtains and draperies of stone and in remote chambers had deposits of dazzling whiteness, but even in the 1840's "wanton depredations of visitors had destroyed most of them."

Huge tables of rock had fallen from the roof, and passages

rock floor and stun him, whereupon Godfrey comes in with a torch and they drag the unconscious man out. He is revealed as "Lieutenant Stranahan," a British spy, complete with papers.

The cave seems to be the one in what is now known as Glen Park, close by the Black River.

were made beneath and above them. The deposits vary from soft, friable rock to marble so hard that when struck it rang like a bell. Here were great pillars and shallow basins filled with limpid water and some slight tufa dams. Hough and a friend went into it an estimated "seventy fathoms" (or about 400 feet) from the chamber at the foot of the entrance and found the water, in June, at 43 degrees. It never freezes in severest winter weather.

The Brownville caves ramify from a sunken place in a wood with various avenues leading underground and connecting. Hough says that almost every natural seam in the rock is large enough for the passage of man and some open into lofty halls. The chambers are in the form of gothic arches, one of them some 30 rods long, but with no limestone formations. Some white flint points thrust from the walls as the sole spectacular feature of the larger cave, but the floor is covered with water and mud.

It is evidently this cavern or these caverns which Judge Phillips attempted to penetrate from the entrance "all the way to Brownville," as tradition had it there was passage, but could not go far in and thinks some of the passages have been closed by nature.

On the west bank of the Perch River that flows from north to south through Limerick and into the lake, quite near the village, is a cavern of curious nature, extending in its first tunnel some 24 yards to emerge into an external passage, then descending 30 feet and going on 63 yards through a passage, both high and low until it becomes a mere crawlway of 154 yards' extent. There were to be found no lateral passages in this Limerick Cave, but Hough wrote that there probably are other caves in the vicinity, but because of the nature of the area they would be of limited extent.

Evidence of other underground hollows in Watertown are to be found in several localities, such as a spot near Pleasant Street where a patch of ground is always bare when there is ice or snow all around it, and suggesting another warm-air cave beneath. Many potholes or sinkholes are to be found in the country around Watertown, such as on the north bank of the Black River opposite what was known of old as Factory Village, where there are several waterworn caves. Other sinkholes in the countryside have been filled by farmers to keep their domestic animals from falling into them.

Hough speaks of the "many fabulous accounts" extant in his time about the caverns of this western state triangle, and Judge Phillips tells of a "legendary spy cave" between Clayton and Cape Vincent and near Millon's Bay on Lake Ontario. It was said to have been used by British spies in the War of 1812. This vicinity, at the head of the St. Lawrence, opposite Kingston, Ontario, would be a likely place for British spies and scouts to roam and seek safe hideouts when in danger of detection. Today the dangers, real or imagined, have curtailed exploration of the caves, but it is likely that the authorities might be persuaded to admit experienced spelunkers into the closed caverns, "at their own risk." The entrance to the Mill Street Bridge Cave is, in fact, now possible, by squirming down through a sidewalk grating in front of the Utilities Building on Moulton Street—but then one must also wriggle through a sewer to get to the natural cave passages.

One of the most promising areas for wild and chilly ice caves appears to be those picturesque wilds in the vicinity of Old Forge, a very rugged, uninhabited region in the western Adirondacks.

Well, anyway, they are most promising on the map. Here we have Ice Cave Mountain, Ice Cave Valley, and Ice Cave Creek. And as if this trio were not wild and blood chilling enough there is also Deadman's Gulch to shiver about and two, count 'em, two Panther Mountains within a few miles of each other, a Moose Mountain, and a Stink Lake Mountain!

Likewise a Cool Mountain, and what a wonderful place to spend hot summer days. All this lies within the Old Forge Quadrangle, as mapped by the U. S. Geological Survey, and most of the shivery features are in Herkimer County, west of

West Canada Lakes, and the Ice Cave Mountain-Valley-Creek features are a few miles southwest of the South Branch of the Moose River. No trails are shown on the map leading to Ice Cave Mountain, which rises to 2,400 feet elevation.

The secret seems to be that all these locations are on the property of the Adirondack League Club, and this club, in its enthusiastic infancy, clapped romantic names, sometimes fanciful ones, upon the geographic features of the area. There is a deep cleft in the rocks on the southern tip of Ice Cave Mountain where ice is found the year round, and exploration of it will require some stout rope and considerable spelunking experience and hardihood. It is a sort of slit, very likely gouged out by glacial action.

Deadman's Gulch, we are informed, is probably possessed of a similar formation, but without the ice, and its story is unknown, but the tradition is that a man was found dead there some years ago.

There is a story about another dead man connected with Deadman's Brook, which is to the west of Little Moose Lake at the foot of Manbury Mountain, and this attaches to French Louie, the trapper of Kun-ja-muck Cave fame, who found the body of a man there and toted the corpse all the way to Lake Pleasant, the county seat, to collect the reward for such noble doings, which amounted to just two dollars per corpse.

But the county officials counted noses of the few inhabitants of their bailiwick and found no one missing, so refused to pay French Louie even the small reward for his trouble. The old trapper is reported to have been so angry that he vowed to use the next body he might find to make sable bait!

The territory in the vicinity of those icy localities may be opened if water power and logging interests succeed in getting permission to cut the timber and build a 3,600-acre reservoir on the State Forest Preserve, but there will be a battle over that, you may be sure.

The "last big log drive" to come out of the Adirondacks, according to official announcement at the time, came tumbling down the swift, steep, Ampersand Creek into the Racquet River in the spring of 1925, when some ten million feet of timber was herded down by a crew of river-rats for the Santa Clara Lumber Company at Tupper Lake. I was there and saw it.

*Glacières* is the French name for ice caves, and a Harvard savant has written a big book about them, having wandered all over Europe seeking these cold places not only in caves but in crevices and the talus of cliffs, etc.[3]

Edwin Swift Balch (Harvard) F.R.G.S., is the man who hunted up a tomeful of ice caves and cracks, beginning when his guide in the White Mountains dug some out of a hole in the side of Mount Adams near Randolph, New Hampshire. He went on from there to investigate them from coast to coast in this country and in Europe. He lists several *glacières* in New York State, including some at Lower Ausable Pond, where ice was found in masses on July 4; in the talus of the Giant of the Valley of the Adirondack Reserve; ice formations and "wind holes" at Watertown; the Snow Hole on Petersburg Mountain; in the Taconics; the Ellenville Ice Caves or gorges; a snow gorge at Sam's Point; and an ice cave near Carlisle. The last two he had only heard of but not seen.

In the talus at the foot of Mount Cobille, or Colvin, Mr. Balch and President Niles, of the Appalachian Mountain Club, found ice in small boulder holes, the temperature so constant that guides use them all summer as refrigerators; and the effect on nature is to make spring flowers bloom in July and even August, by producing an "artificial climate."

Balch also observed the caves at Watertown, close together, one icy, the other blowing out warm air, a phenomenon of unusual type. The ice cave was a beer storage cellar when he visited it in 1899.

A man-made hole in the ground, dug for a well, became a "freezing well," according to an account in an ancient book on *Ice Caves,* by Rev. G. F. Browne, who published it in 1865 in

[3] *Glacières or Freezing Caverns,* Edwin Swift Balch, 1900, Allen Lane & Scott, Phila.

London. This was located near the town of Owego, three-quarters of a mile from the Susquehanna River, and the account is quoted from no less an authority than the *American Journal of Science,* chap. 36, p. 184, which describes this curious phenomenon thus:

> The depth of the well is 77 feet and for four or five months in the year the surface of the water is frozen so hard as to render the well useless. Large masses of ice have been found late in July. A thermometer, which stood at 68 degrees in the sun, fell to 30 degrees in fifteen minutes at the bottom of the well; the men who made the well were forced to put on thick clothing in June, and even so could not work for more than two hours at a time. No other well in that neighborhood presents the same phenomenon. A lighted candle was let down, and the flame became agitated and thrown in one direction at a depth of 30 feet, but was quite still at the bottom, where, however, it soon died out. The water is hard limestone water.

Scientists have been puzzled to explain why some ice caves appear to form ice in summer rather than in winter. The most common explanation is that the cold of winter does not penetrate through the rocks and narrow passages between them until summer because it only slowly works its way down.

# *Chapter XVII*

# SOME MIGHTY MAN-MADE CAVES[1]

FEW persons think of New York State as being a mining empire, but such it is and was even more so in the past. In the discoveries of ores, especially iron ores, there grew up a typical "western" mining town that took on the obvious name of Mineville, for instance, having at one time the largest and most productive mines in the state. Port Henry was the shipping port and site of the blast furnace, Moriah, a century ago, when charcoal was used exclusively in the processing of ore. The ruins of the Coburn furnace near Mineville may yet be found, as may those of other furnaces constructed by hand labor.

A report on *The Mineville-Port Henry Mine Group,* written by James P. Kemp, and published by the State Education Department in 1908, refers to a dozen iron mines and shows their locations on a large-scale map. They are scattered from Lake Champlain on the east to Crowfoot Pond on the west, and from Port Henry on the south to the vicinity of Four Ponds on the north, an area of about 100 square miles. At this period two companies were operating the Mineville iron centers and had produced an estimated 25,000,000 tons of ore. One mine, closed, was to be reopened, and the report stated that "There is no sign of exhaustion, and thus the amount of iron originally present in these deposits makes them rank well up among the great ore bodies of the world."

The ore was discovered in the 1830s and '40s, and the old bloomeries or forges were located where there was water-power to run the blast and the trip hammer. Ore was sometimes

1 "Cave—A hollow in the earth either natural or man-made."—Webster.

hauled by ox-team for many miles to these furnaces, and most of it was shipped out by water, until the railroads built spurs into the minefields.

Photographs of Mineville taken at the 1908 period show huge open shafts or cuts with horizontal shafts running out of them, beneath the rude structures of the then tiny town with its background of wooded hills, denuded partly, stripped again and again for the wood to make charcoal.

But it is not the purpose of this chapter to describe the mineralogy, geology and mechanics of the mines, which may be read in scientific treatises to the heart's content—or the brain's weariness—and the human stories of some typical old mining towns and fields furnish a richer sort of ore from our Underground Empire.

The most fascinating story of New York's iron mines is doubtless, "The Story of Crown Point Iron," a chapter in *The Rise and Decline of Local Industry in the United States,* by E. Eugene Barker, Ph.D. Mr. Barker's original report was published by the New York State Historical Society in its magazine, *New York History,* in 1941. But an unpublished appendix and a map furnish some of the richest human interest to this intensely fascinating story, centering around the now completely abandoned town of Hammondville, where yawn the dead mouths of a family of iron mines, feeding upon rank vegetation as the wilderness has come back to reclaim its own.

Benedict Arnold, in command of the Crown Point Fort in 1775, sent a boatload of Negroes to dig iron ore from the Cheever Mine, which was being worked as early as 1766, when Major Philip Skene shipped many boatloads of ore from it to his forges at Skenesboro. The Cheever ore was made into iron for fitting out vessels that were engaged in the first naval battle in the Revolution, and out of these mines came the ore for wartime uses in 1812, 1845, and the 1860's.

New discoveries were made rapidly, among them some accidental ones which add to the human interest of the Crown Point story.

One day in 1806 a man, name forgotten, saw some bluish mineral uncovered by the falling of a pine tree, its roots tearing out the soil. It was a bed of fine iron ore from which the finder made himself a small bar of iron at a blacksmith shop at Jay, to prove his find. This was later known as the famous Arnold Hill bed in Peru, New York.

The Hammond bed in Crown Point was bumped into by a bee-hunter, roaming the wilderness, who filled his pockets with ore, and later he and helpers toted out eight or ten hundred pounds for a mile on their backs to a road, whence it was carted to Ticonderoga.

A boy, hunting partridges, grabbed hold of a bush to pull himself up the steep mountainside, on a day in 1826, and he uprooted himself a fortune in shining iron ore, took samples to his father who opened a mine, and then sold it to Penfield and Taft. This Penfield bed was worked for about forty years before it was exhausted.

The story of iron in York State is tied up with the story of the development of the electric motor by Joseph Henry, for in 1831 the Crown Point Company secured an electro-magnet from Professor Henry of the Albany Academy for what is believed to have been the first industrial use of electricity anywhere. It was used for lifting iron in the separation process at the forges. Charles Franklin Hammond was the spark plug of the workings, which became known as Hammondville, and he associated himself with Jonas Tower, an expert furnace man, who, with C. F. and J. C. Hammond and Allen Penfield, built a furnace midway between the ore deposits and ledges of limestone in the rugged mountain country where there was plenty of wood for making charcoal, pure spring water in abundance, and ample space for a settlement to be. This was in 1844-45, the first iron being run from the furnace January 1, 1846. This stone and brick structure stood 45 feet high and was 9 feet across at the base, a very small one by modern standards, but from it came ore that became famous. The first steel made in this country under Bessemer patents is said to have been made from "Hammond ore" exclusively, at Troy.

The old furnace was burned down in 1865, rebuilt at once, but abandoned in 1872 as new furnaces were erected at the shore of Champlain—for one good reason because of the "inexhaustible" wood supply had almost vanished from the vicinity, the operations consuming 650,000 bushels of charcoal a year!

As in our later wars, production was stepped up mightily, especially during the Civil War. Crown Point Iron went into the armor of the warship "Monitor," to revolutionize naval warfare.

There was beauty at these furnaces, despite the rape of the woods; even the road to the old Hammond furnaces was "formed by a very beautiful material," as described by Winslow Eaton in 1852.

Walking the surface was like treading on rainbows, the slag being "soft and lustrous and glowing in every shade and tint." In drawing out the glass on a wire, Mr. Watson observed that it "presents a most delicate and diversified coloring . . . beautiful in its crude and adulterated condition," and asked, prophetically, "May not this substance, purified and refined by science, be rendered subservient to the arts?"

Visitors of these latter days, wandering about the abandoned areas of Hammondville and Crown Point, may pick up beautiful pieces of this colorful slag, looking as fresh and glowing as they were a century ago; and old, winding roads still remain because they were paved with the metallic mineral and are repaired by it from the old dumps.

But to look down into some of the great, dark holes, open shafts with towering cliffs between which a rank, spindly growth of birches and poplars and weed trees have grown, or in some cases have closed almost over a dark, yawning tunnel, is sufficient for the average visitor, although the more bold and curious with spelunking habits and inclinations, may yet wander into the dark interiors for long distances and see mines that have truly reverted to nature and become caverns.

An effort to revive the mining after the first closing down in the 1890's was made in 1901 by the American Steel and Wire Company that had bought the properties at public bankruptcy sale, but the effort was not profitable, and the mines, furnaces, and buildings were again abandoned, never to see the glare of the roaring fires against the sky again. Year by year the machinery rusted, houses lapsed into ruin, weeds grew in the slag between the railroad tracks, young trees sprang up and grew tall enough to screen the growing desolation. Most of the usable machinery was eventually shipped out, the rest sold for scrap, the railroad torn up, and in 1905 the furnaces leveled, leaving only lofty brick towers, for a few years, to mark the landscape until they, too, tumbled down and were raked over for their materials for building elsewhere. Mr. Barker writes:

> Today, remains of any of these numerous and formerly conspicuous works can hardly be traced. Winding mounds and earth cuts where trains of ore and passengers used to pass will always mark the trail of the railroad, though in places they are already overgrown with sizeable trees.
>
> At Ironville, now a hamlet, without even a postoffice name, stone abutments of the dam that formerly held the pond can be found in the bushes which encroach on the waters of the creek. . . . At the mines where the village of Hammondville stood on the mountain top, with its powerhouses, hoists, store, office, two churches and numerous dwellings, only the partial walls of a stone powder-house remain. Where that community flourished there is now pasture, fast being taken over by raspberry and blueberry bushes and sapling birches. Fearsome, yawning chasms of the open mines, here and there on the mountain top, some of them already hidden in dense woods, still remain to excite the imagination of the casual visitor and to challenge some antiquarian to a hazardous day's exploration among the concealing thickets and repossessing forests.[2]

The fame of a name that has for many years been a symbol of truly rural rusticity hangs upon Podunk Pond, a real place, with a real history. Podunk is not just a vaudeville joke. Podunk Pond is still on the map, although the village of that name has

[2]See Appendix for further interesting details of the once mighty iron empire.

vanished, leaving no trace. It was the last retreat of the Podunk Indians, allies of the Narragansetts, and who fought with them in King Philip's War.

In a historical discourse titled *Life of Uncas,* by William L. Stone, published in 1842 after being delivered by the author as a reading at Norwich, Connecticut, on the Fourth of July of that year, the following footnote appears:

> The Podunk Indians in the time of King Philip's War numbered between two and three hundred men. They went into the contest with Philip and were never heard of afterward.

But the local residents of the vicinity of Podunk Pond, which is in the western part of Washington County, knew of the Podunk Indians. The remnant of the tribe left after the wars, fled from New England to the fastnesses of the Adirondacks, settled on the shores of this small lake and evidently lived there until they died out. Authority for this local history is a gentleman named Granger of West Fort Ann, who told A. T. Shorey some years ago that his father had informed him that the pond was named for the Podunk Indians who settled in the valley between Lake George and Lake Champlain. Podunk Pond is connected with Lakes Pond, named for a Sergeant Lake who was a member of Rogers' Rangers and was awarded a grant of land for his heroic services with that fighting outfit. The Mohegans, with other allies, fought the Mohawks throughout this area, and left their names in Mohegan Island and Uncas Island and other places in and around Lake George; but the solitary place name memento to the Podunks is the little lake in the woods where, today, "tribes" of Boy Scouts and Girl Scouts roam about at Indian games in summer.

The Podunks are not mentioned as being at the Battle of Lake George in September, 1755, although it was right up through their valley that General Dieskau marched to the battle, to be defeated by English troops and Mohawk Indians and captured. It is believed the Podunks had vanished before this time.

Near Podunk Pond is a small cave with some faint tradition of being once used as a shelter, maybe by the last of the Podunks.

There is probably no other name as commonly used in jest, unless it is Squeedunk, a legendary place in Maine to which bores are consigned when they become too great a nuisance.

Mount Hope Mine yawns with three gaping black mouths in a rock cliff, containing magnetite ore that was highly valued in the early days of the iron and steel industry, and still is, but it is not mined here any more, nor in others of the chain of iron mines that once made up an eastern empire underground. The cessation of the industry was due largely to the limited quantities and production costs, in comparison to the huge open-cut or strip-iron mines of the West and Northwest.

Approach to the mine is via various rambling country roads leading off the highway from Glens Falls (U. S. 9L) which passes through Fort Ann, a four-corners settlement of a few houses, a dozen miles northeast of Glens Falls, from which there ambles off a road that has many turnings, crossroads, side roads, and dead ends, requiring close study of a large-scale topographic map and directions from one who has visited the area and jotted down notes of the turnings and landmarks. "Streaked House Corner," for instance, is a critical point of usual confusion to the stranger seeking the mine.

An expedition for hiking and spelunking purposes made on a brilliant Sunday, September 22, 1946, proved a picturesque and somewhat exciting field day for all, and almost disastrous for some—not at all inside the huge mine, but in the wide outdoors, on narrow roads—one of them having reverted to no more than a foot trail.

One purpose of the expedition was to discover whether the Mount Hope Mine might possibly be a suitable site as a shelter or area for military installations in case of atomic war, and the National Speleological Society was so interested that the President, William J. Stephenson, and Elton Brown, Chairman of the Safety and Equipment Committee, drove from Washington, D. C., to join the party, A bus load of members of the Albany Chapter, Adirondack Mountain Club, and Mohawk

Valley Hiking Club of Schenectady, met the N.S.S. officials at the trail entrance.

Iron mines stretched from New Jersey far up into the Adirondacks in the early nineteenth century, and their history would fill a big book in itself, but this history is being slowly lost, "in the mists of antiquity" and may never be written. What fragments of the story of this string of mines can be included here touch only upon what might be called typical interests of once thriving mines which have long been abandoned.

Such as the ancient Mount Hope Iron Mine (which had another name) located halfway up the rocky side of a low mountain in West Fort Ann, which is certainly a ghost town if it ever had much flesh and bones. The principal inhabitants of the woods-enclosed area are now Girl Scouts and Boy Scouts, who have camps in the vinicity of Podunk Pond and Lakes Pond; and the Albany Girl Scout organization has an abandoned mine on its hands as well as some hundreds of acres of forest land.

A three-quarters of a mile hike over a road that once had borne tons of magnetite ore, drawn by oxen to a forge near Podunk Pond, brought the party of some thirty persons to the black, yawning mouths of the mine, one of them leading far into the side of the hill. The utterly black walls, roof, and floor made strong carbide lights seem feeble, and some of the hikers preferred to remain outside in the sun.

The way was on the level, save for here and there sudden depressions filled with water as black as the floor and upper shelves and adits from which the precious ore had been painfully carved and blasted. The workings extended about one-eighth of a mile into the hill, and the miners had cut up and out at the extreme end, perhaps to furnish circulation of air against the fumes of blasting powder.

One of the party included the eminent young scientist, Vincent J. Schaefer. Mr. Schaefer became much interested in a phenomenon which occurred in this old mine. When the party entered all was clear, but upon turning back to stumble out, they ran into a dense fog, due to intense humidity in the air that came in from outside to meet the chill of the mine. Mr. Schaefer later revealed that an artificial rainstorm might have been made in the fog with his dry-ice treatment, or the fog dissipated by the same procedure, a tip for air-conditioning if ever the United States Engineering Corps finds it advisable to develop this black hole of West Fort Ann into a war factory.

Adventures came thick and fast that day, with a belated party from Springfield, Massachusetts, headed by Roger Johnson, plunging into the patch of woods from opposite where we had entered and twice getting hung up on rock ledges of an old road with their car, but—as is usual with this Yankee caveman—getting out under his own power despite a flat tire. Chance meetings at crossroads saved Miss Lydia Neubuck, from the Natural Stone Bridge at Pottersville, from being stranded, and altogether the party decided that there must be some magnetic influence around the old Mount Hope Mine.

Mount Hope Mine is an historical example of the series of iron mines that runs up from New Jersey, through the Ramapo Highlands into the Adirondacks. It was opened by the famous Baron Hasenclever, a German-born patriot, and S. S. Smith, equally famous in the mining world of England. The latter, an expert, came from the Forester-Dean Mines in that country to open a huge iron mine in the Ramapos which he named for the old company.[3]

[3]Baron Peter Hasenclever was a man of big business, ahead of his time. In 1763 he organized a company in London, with a capital of forty thousand pounds, to go to America and produce pig iron, hemp, and potash. In June, 1764, he arrived in New York, followed by miners and ironworkers he had hired in England, and immediately started a veritable iron empire, beginning in Morris County, New Jersey, and within two years had acquired 4 blast furnaces, 7 forges, 235 stores, workshops and dwelling houses, 13 millponds, 10 bridges, and many miles of roads. He was called Baron because he lived in regal splendor in an elegant home at Ringwood, from whence he directed his vast works. Suddenly, in 1769, he left for London to try to reassure his backers, who had become frightened at his expenditures. They refused to support him further. He returned, to declare himself a bankrupt; but he set up shop again in Landeshut, Germany, regained his fortune, and was a wealthy man when he died in 1793.

(This biographical material is furnished by *Steelways*, published by the American Iron & Steel Institute.)

Mount Hope Mine was operated continuously until after the Civil War, when litigation that dragged on for years brought to the owners a New York City attorney's bill for thirty thousand dollars.

The story is that the owners looked at the bill and said, "We have won the suit, you can have the mine and the whole damned property."

The shrewd lawyer took it over and reaped a fortune—not from iron but from wood. He logged off the 2,800-acre tract of hardwood more than once.

Histories are rather vague about the mining industry at Fort Ann. A *Gazeteer of Washington County* by Allen Corey, 1849-50, makes no mention of Mount Hope Mine but admits to a forge and anchor shop conducted by Caleb Kingsley. *French's Gazeteer of the State of New York,* 1866, says only that a blast furnace was built at Mount Hope[4] in 1826 that made five tons of pig iron daily, and that a forge was built at West Fort Ann in 1828 for making anchors and chains. These authorities differ widely as to the origin of Fort Ann itself. It was a citadel of defense against Indians. French's book dates it as 1709, and Corey's as 1757!

But Burgoyne's military road ran through here, two miles south of Fort Ann village, in 1777, and there was a rude log palisade here, one of a chain that was erected through the wilderness, by the French. They were burned by Burgoyne.

The old Champlain Canal ran through Fort Ann, and one of its accomplishments was to bring some 3,100 persons to reside here in 1810. So are the mighty fallen.

[4]There is an interesting mystery about the naming of Mount Hope. The "furnace builder," Smith-Sayre, who built the Mount Hope furnace, started his work in New Jersey and moved north, and at each furnace site he named a Mount Hope. But, curiously, the seat of King Philip when he was in power was at Sowanset near "Mon-Top," or Mount Hope, memorable as the citadel of this chieftan, whose allies, the Podunks "fled to the west," and settled in West Fort Ann. Perhaps they brought the name with them long before the ironworkers came.

## *Chapter XVIII*

# SALT OF THE EARTH

A GEOLOGIST, in 1885, estimated that there were areas of New York State underlaid with salt, aggregating 1,100 miles in extent; but a later study, issued in 1928, declares that such estimates as this are of no great importance, in that they would be at best mere guesses based upon inadequate data.[1]

This report also declares that there is an excessive tonnage of salt within the limits of the state and that there is an almost inexhaustible supply of it.

Since we are here concerned with salt mines or man-made caverns, we need not bore our readers by boring into the numerous "brine wells" which draw salt water up from Silurian depths and evaporate it to get salt. There are but two rocksalt mines in operation now in the state, one at Retsof, near Warsaw and Rochester, and one at Cayuga Lake. The Retsof Mine, owned by the International Salt Company, is most interesting, being a collection of mines, joined together, that extend beneath the town of Warsaw and around it, with an estimated 120 miles of underground tunnels.

The mine is a beautiful place, for the rock salt is so pure and white, so firm, dry, and non-crumbling, that even the office at the mine is cut out of solid salt, and here foremen and draftsmen work in a steady 63-degree temperature, summer and winter, with no artificial heat required. Nearby is one of the most complete machine shops in the country, also hewn out of the saline rock, and down below, over 1,000 feet, in a bed of salt 18 feet thick, workmen enjoy mining as if in a parlor.

The mine area covers over 1,000 acres, and a circuit of its

[1] *The Geology and Origin of the Silurian Salt of New York State*, by Harold L. Alling. N. Y. State Museum Bulletin No. 275, 1928.

electric railroad takes one for 15 miles, some of the corridors extending for *more than a mile and a half in one direction.*

Only 67 percent of the salt is taken out as workmen carve their way into this vast vein. The rest is left for pillars and walls to support the roof. The gangways and rooms in the mine are huge, some of them 55 feet wide, a veritable three-lane highway, deep underground. Pillars left standing are 55 by 200 feet in dimension.

Here are huge machines such as are used in modern coal mines, but requiring tougher drills and knives, for rock salt is harder to cut than coal. Electricity is used throughout the mine, with dynamite to blast out blocks of the material in places. Undercutting is the first opertaion and an ingenious and dramatic one. A powerful machine with a saw-like projection to it, double-edged, a band saw, really, for the blade is an endless belt with large, sharp teeth of high-grade tool steel, first cuts a horizontal slot in the salt wall, at the level of the gangway floor. It is made 10 feet deep and 55 feet across. There follow the various other operations, of sideshearing, drilling, blasting, loading, and transportation. Trains of trams pulled by electric locomotives run rumbling over the rails, piled with hunks of the salt. These trains are from 20 to 25 cars and are hauled by 8-ton, 10-ton and 15-ton electric locomotives to the shaft bottom, and there dumped into a great grinder or sifter of bars that separate the fine from the lumps. The large lumps are crushed at the mine bottom and then carried to the 7-ton skips to the top for further crushing and screening.

Rock salt is shipped away as fast as it is mined, no storage being made at the mines, nor are there any purifying processes done; it is merely prepared for the market in this swift and efficient manner. Practically the same processes are used in rock-salt mines all over the country.

Rock-salt mining in New York is the oldest established industry of its sort in the country. It was first mentioned in the *Jesuit Relations* and the first discovery is credited to Father Le Moyne, a French Jesuit, in 1653, through contact with the

Indians, who got it from salt springs, some of which are still flowing.

The manufacture of salt by white people began near Syracuse about 1788, but it was not until 1865 that rock salt was found at the village of Vincent, western Ontario County. Only three years earlier the first rock salt in the United States had been discovered at Avery Island, Lousiana, a deposit that was of vital importance during the Civil War.

The first shaft was sunk at Retsof in 1885 and used until 1922, when a new one was made, much larger. It is elliptical in shape, 9 feet wide by 28 feet long, and is lined with concrete for its total extent down to the 1,073-foot level in the 18-foot bed that is being worked. It has three compartments, of which two are used for hoisting salt and one for the men and supplies. The skips or elevators literally skip up at a speed that brings their loads to the breaker building at the top, a fifth of a mile, in just 55 seconds.

It is a far cry from the potash kettles at the primitive salt works at Salt Point, later named Salina, on the shores of Onondaga Lake, used by William Val Vleck and Moses De Witt, in 1793, the first regular salt works in New York State, to this mammoth underground factory.

Here is an ideal place to work, for the air is conditioned, being naturally dry, and the breathing in of salty air has proved healthful; indeed, a preventive of colds and other respiratory diseases. Such mines as this should prove models for underground military installations, war factories and shelters which the Government is now seeking as defensive sites in case of atomic war.

The latest official report upon the amount of salt mined or pumped up as brine and evaporated, was issued in 1939 by the geologists of the New York State Museum. It reveals that from 1797 to 1939 a total of almost 80,000,000 tons had been produced, with a value of almost $105,000,000.[2]

Salt is used not only to keep people alive, for upon the normal

[2]New York State Museum Bulletin No. 315, 1918.

three ounces of salt contained in the human body depends life, nor is it confined to flavoring food, though that is one of its important and delicious uses. One of its more recent uses is to thaw out ice and snow on city streets. Rock salt is used for this. It bores down into the ice and compacted snow, breaks them up, and gives us bare streets shortly after being spread, thereby proving an economical means of removing winter's layers and providing swift safety for motorists after big storms. Some cities use salt exclusively for this purpose on their paved streets, abandoning snow-plowing, snow-loading, trucking and hand labor entirely.

At least two cities, in the hard winter of 1945, proved that a "salt storm" following a snow storm was the best way to remove "the beautiful" from their streets. Hartford, Connecticut, citizens, waking one morning after a snowfall which they believed would bury their streets so deep that it was useless even to try to drive down into the city's center were astonished to find that downtown Hartford's streets were as bare as in summer, that busses were running on schedule, and an 18-inch precipitation had vanished as if by magic.

In Clarksburg, West Virginia, the same year, the automobile club gave away 10-pound bags of rock salt to motorists to use if they got stuck on snow-rutted roads or on ice, the salt to be thrown under spinning wheels, acting, first, as an abrasive, like sand, then as a thawing agency. In Clarksburg, later, the streets were sprinkled with salt water, a 70-percent solution.

Rock salt is also useful for removing soot from chimneys by throwing it onto the coal fire, a nutrient for crops, a weed-killer, in combination with other chemicals, as an ingredient in tanning leather, dyeing cloth, manufacturing china, glass, paper, plastics, steel, ceramics, and many other products.

In the manufacture of steel, salt has its most spectacular use. In the great foundries where huge molten steel blocks are produced at tremendous temperatures rock salt is used to remove the scale which forms as the glowing ingots begin to cool, and it is also necessary in the processing of copper, silver, lead, and other metals. A chart, showing the varied uses of salt in agriculture, industry, medicine and the home, issued by the International Salt Company, reveals over two hundred uses for this precious "salt of the earth." One of them is in the manufacture of war munitions. Chlorine, a derivative of salt, is important in this, as it is in purifying drinking water for most of the cities and towns in this country and others.

Such are some of the novel uses of the stuff that is dug out of these man-made caverns, costing but a few cents a pound in its refined state, yet worth its weight in gold to mankind.

# APPENDIX

## *The Origin of Caverns*

What is the origin of caverns? In layman's language it is merely from "the action of water running and eroding and dissolving limestones or other comparatively soluble rock." That is to form a "true cave" as compared with one accidentally fashioned from tumbled rock or a split from an earth tremor or from frost.

An excellent geological explanation of caves and caverns was given by Dr. Edward S. C. Smith, head of the Geology Department, Union College, Schenectady, in a broadcast over Station WGY in the General Electric Science Forum series, October 29, 1940, which we have permission to publish. It is appropriate to New York State caverns as well as others.

> Caves and caverns! What tales of mystery and romance are suggested by these words. Probably no other single topic in earth science so stimulates and intrigues the human imagination. Caves have been the dwellings of prehistoric men and the haunts of real or mythical robber bands. A cave may in turn have been the hiding place of the escaped slave or the sanctuary of the hermit. But as man in recent times has turned to the study and exploration of these subterranean openings he has found his imagination the more stimulated and his curiosity the more aroused by the wonders of the natural processes by whose action the development of caves and caverns has been brought about.
>
> For the purposes of this discussion we will define a cave as a cavity, usually of natural origin, beneath the earth's surface and ordinarily of no great extent. A cavern, on the other hand, will be understood to be a large subterranean cavity usually of greater depth, and always of greater size than a cave, often with many chambers and connecting passages which may be traced for considerable distances.
>
> The Luray Caverns of Virginia are among the best known in the world, having been open to the public continually since 1878. Here huge chambers 30 to 90 feet high are to be found at four different levels, all connected by an intricate series of natural passageways extending for several miles. Other famous caverns will come instantly to mind, such as the Mammoth Cave (it should be called a Cavern) in Kentucky, the Carlsbad Caverns in New Mexico, the Howe Caverns of New York State, and a host of others. What is the process, or what are the agencies by which these caverns have been formed?

## *UNDERGROUND EMPIRE*

A cave, to use the term in its most inclusive sense, may be merely a shelter under a fallen granite slab, or a shallow alcove which has resulted from stream erosion of the bedrock. Cooper's Cave at Glens Falls, N. Y., is in this latter category. Caves along the shores of lakes or the sea are by no means uncommon, the result of the constant beating by the waves upon the weaker rocks. Caves may occur also under lava flows, when the upper portion cools quickly and allows the lower part, still liquid, to flow out, leaving a hardened shell above.

Caves may be found in nearly any type of rock in which vertical joint planes have been developed. These may become widened and deepened by weathering or by minor earth movements. However, the word cavern always implies depth and extent underground, and the production of such a feature requires a rather definite set of factors in place and time. But, given those essential factors, the caverns will develop. First, we must have as the bedrock a mass of at least moderately thick limestone, which, further, must cover a fairly large area and be relatively undisturbed, that is, if we are to have an extensive cavern system, for limestones are the only rocks appearing in appreciable quantities at and near the earth's surface which are soluble at ordinary temperatures and pressures, and it is upon this property of solubility that we lean most heavily for the explanation of cavern formation.

To understand the origin of caverns it is necessary first to refresh our memory on the general subject of ground water.

When rain falls upon the surface of the earth a part of it is immediately evaporated and returned to the atmosphere from whence it came, another part is absorbed by the vegetation, another part forms the run-off, so called, which finds its way into the streams and rivers, but much of the water enters the pores of the surface materials and, drawn downward by the pull of gravity, passes into the naturally occurring crevices and fissures of the solid bedrock. This downward migration of the water will ordinarily continue until some impervious material is reached or until it reaches a zone where the rocks are completely saturated. This saturated zone is present nearly everywhere at varying depths below ground, and the water occupying it is called the ground water. The upper surface of this saturated zone is called the water table. It is then, this water moving ever downward toward the zone of saturation that is commonly believed to be such an important factor in the formation of caverns. The rain water always has more or less carbon dioxide dissolved in it which it obtains from the atmosphere, and such a solution of carbon dioxide is an effective solvent for most limestones; thus, when such water charged with carbon dioxide passes through the joint planes or bedding planes in limestone, the rock will be slowly dissolved. Eventually this water reaches the ground-water level and here, theoretically at least, the water should be so saturated with lime that no more could be taken into solution. That some solution does take place below the level of the water table seems probable, as there is a continu-

The Retsof Salt Mine has 120 miles of deep underground tunnels like this, and its own electric railroad

Members of the Legislature, known as the Ostertag Committee, formed to advise the Governor on problems of an economic nature common to several states, watch a machine start sawing salt in the Retsof Mine

Giant pothole at Little Falls—looking out. Believed the largest yet found in the world

ous, though slow circulation of the ground waters themselves, and there is no proof that the ground water in limestone regions is always saturated. In fact some investigators have proposed the possibility of much solution below the water table, subsequent elevation of the region resulting in the draining out and exposure of the extensive solution openings. It is generally believed, however, that most caverns are formed above the level of the water table. As solution continues along joint fissures and bedding planes, large underground passages and huge chambers are formed, through many of which flow streams of water, some of notable size. Eventually as an underground drainage system becomes well developed the surface drainage tends to disappear and rain immediately finds its way underground through the joints or through depressions called sinks which result from the enlargement of intersecting joints or occasionally from the actual collapse of cavern roofs.

In the State of Kentucky is an area underlain by cavernous limestones estimated at about 8,000 square miles, and here the absence of surface-flowing streams over much of this region is perhaps the most remarkable feature of the landscape. At lower levels, where surface streams do not exist, one frequently sees a tributary stream emerging from beneath the limestone walls of the valley.

It is easy to see that the development of such an extensive cavern system will have a very definite effect upon the topography. Not only do rivers disappear and reappear in a disconcerting way, but careless agricultural methods or deforestation may allow the soil to be washed down into the caverns and thus be lost forever, while exposed limestone surfaces will be deeply trenched by erosion. Hence vegetation may be scant or absent altogether, especially in a not too humid climate.

In regions of cavernous limestone such surface phenomena as sinkholes, disappearing streams, and solution valleys become very numerous and the topography most characteristic. This has been called karst topography from the Karst region of Yugoslavia where it is strongly developed. Topography which approaches the karst type is also found in Kentucky, Tennessee, Indiana and Florida in the United States, in southern France, in Yucatan and elsewhere.

The eventual fate of a great limestone region would seem to be its entire destruction. For with underground drainage firmly established the solution of the limestone would continue, sinks would enlarge and coalesce, surface solution would consume other portions until at last the entire region would be reduced to the level of the streams which had established themselves in the formerly existing caverns. The completion of such an ideal cycle assumes that the rainfall and general climatic conditions remain stable and that no great elevation or subsidence of the land as a whole takes place. This theoretical cycle of formation and destruction of limestone caverns has been called the cavern cycle. There are, it should be remembered, many varying factors which condition the amount of solution that takes place in a given cavern, such as the temperature of the water, the atmospheric pressure, and the amount of carbon dioxide in the water.

Up to now we have concerned ourselves with the solvent action of the rain water charged with carbon dioxide as it dissolves away the limestone in the process of cavern making. As the chambers and passages enlarge and abundant air penetrates them, this water trickling down the walls and dripping from the ceilings has an opportunity to rid itself, in part at least, of its dissolved load of mineral matter, for as the water evaporates in open chasms the mineral salts are given up and deposits of lime carbonate, commonly called dripstone, begin to accumulate. Dripstone is formed in open cavities above the water table and as its name implies is formed by the dripping of water from the roofs and sides of caverns or passages. The process is not difficult to understand: water carrying lime carbonate in solution moves slowly along the roof of the cavern and some of it evaporates leaving a little mineral matter deposited at the spot. Drop by drop more lime carbonate is added, and, in the same manner that icicles grow from the eaves of a house, so do these "mineral icicles" grow from the roof of a cave. Such downward hanging "mineral icicles" are called stalactites. Corresponding forms built up from the floor are called stalagmites. Occasionally the stalactite above will unite with the stalagmite below, forming a column. The stalagmite growing from the floor of a cavern results from the accumulation of the mineral matter which may still remain in the drops of water which fall from the growing stalactites.

Water seeping slowly down the cavern walls may produce great sheets of deposited mineral matter called flowstone. All of these formations may assume curious and fantastic shapes and, sometimes, colored by various substances which may also be in solution, lend a weird and beautiful appearance to these structures. It is quite impossible adequately to describe in words the beauty of these many marvelous forms, which must be seen to be truly appreciated. Chemically all of this mineral material is calcium carbonate in the form called by the mineralogist travertine.

Caves and caverns have always been to a greater or less degree the habitation of animals and in the early days of the human race by man himself. Caverns are often rich in animal remains ranging all the way from the guano of modern bats to the complete skeletons of animals long since extinct. Certain of the caves of southern France may in reality be called our oldest art galleries, for upon their walls there appear in charcoal and in brightly colored mineral paints the representations delineated by primitive man of many different types of animals that roamed Europe just after the close of the last great ice age. It is interesting to note that while some of these sketches are surprisingly true to life, they lack that most important feature of modern drawing, namely, perspective.

Cavern hunting and exploring in regions whose limestone forma-

**tions afford access underground, has today become the sport of amateurs as well as of professionals, and it is recruiting an ever increasing number of enthusiasts any one of whom has a chance to discover—who knows what new amazing phenomenon in Nature's storehouse of secrets.**

## *The Geology of Taconic Cave Country*

The question of the geology of the Taconic Range is not easy to answer because it involves many complex problems as yet unsettled. However, it is safe to say that the Taconic Range in New York involves the same problems as that of New England. The entire Taconic problem involves, we are convinced, a series of overthrusts. As one progresses from the west to the east, metaphorism becomes progressively more advanced. In the western part the formations involved are shales with some limestone and grit, ranging in age from Lower Cambrian up to Middle Ordovician. The frequent belts of limestone in the series present a problem as yet unsolved. Some of these may represent fenesters; that is, erosion down to the bedrock upon the surface of which the Taconic overthrust moved.

There are occurrences of this type, particularly those in the Poughkeepsie area, which certainly cannot be interpreted in this way, but are, I believe, portions of the underlying limestones which were caught up in the sole of the overthrust, folded into the overthrust mass, and moved with it westward and upward.

Dr. Balk has written a beautiful paper on the Poughkeepsie area and adjacent regions in New York but has accepted as a premise the idea that he is dealing with the normal sections, with limestones at the bottom of the series which are exposed in many of the valleys of that region, and that these formations are capped by shales. In tracing the beds eastward, the shales become more and more metamorphosed. Our findings indicate, however, that the mass of the metamorphosed shales belong to the Nassau beds and Lower Cambrian and are not the equivalent of those of the Snake Hill age which lie normally upon the limestones, the youngest of which are Trenton in that area.

BY DR. ROUSSEAU H. FLOWER,
*Assistant State Paleontologist of New York*

Richard F. Logan, who has studied the geology of the Taconics on both sides, says that in the case of such caves as Indian Oven in Millerton, and passages under No Bottom Pond in Austerlitz, which he has visited, the cave or caves occur in a rather thin bed of limestone, interbedded between layers of schist, which was originally mud. They represent a period when the region was submerged by the sea, but was close to the shoreline along which streams were depositing muds, indicating that there was rain on the land to the east, and slopes down which streams bore mud. The beds of limestone indicate periods of lower land and drier weather when the water along the shore became clearer and the chemical deposition of lime ooze and accumulation of limey shells of marine organisms took the place of mud banks. These beds are present in the schist at several places in eastern York State and in the hills across the border, too. Limestone is soluble but schist is not, hence the schist rock remains, towering above the beds of limestone, and the valleys on both sides of the Taconics are partly a result of the dissolution of limestone and are usually caveless because they are too near the water table. Caves on high places are formed faster by drainage and chemical action dissolving passages through the limestone.

> The great warm sea which, at one time, we are told, covered the eastern part of the United States, as far as the Helderberg Range, formed the narrow strip of limestone of the Taconics from dissolved calcium carbonate. It is extracted from solution by purely chemical reactions, by the intervention of minute plants (algae) or by various shell-forming animals (corals, clams, etc.).[1]

Mr. Logan closely studied such caverns in the Taconics as Indian Oven, Bentley's Cavern, and others.

A surprising, comparatively swift change in Indian Oven Cavern was discovered in the summer of 1946. Within ten years a waterfall that had existed there had vanished. The flowing stream had carved down through one bed of limestone and dropped upon another below, out of sight, a minute example of the "suicide" of caves.

In the report of the State Geologist, published by the New York State Education Department, New York State Museum, in 1906, Professor John H. Cook, who made a field study of Eastern New York caves, gives the following concise explanation of how caves "grow."

[1]From *New England's Buried Treasure.*

The diameter attained by a cave is primarily dependent upon the amount of water passing through it and the relative solubility of the rock. The life of a cave ends when the roof gives way and the channel is opened to day, a fate which may overtake it early in its development or be postponed for a long time, but it is inevitable. As the cavity is enlarged beneath thin or loosely coherent beds, these, deprived of support fall into it and unless beds sufficiently firm to maintain their position lie above, the cavern will speedily be reduced to a ruin. Such "dead" caverns have a notable effect on topography, produce small sinkholes or large rock basins without outlet or inlet. Though dead as caverns these areas may still be active fields of solution and erosion. Some instructive instances of such topographic forms, *Karsten,* resulting from the falling in of caverns are to be seen on the Helderberg plateau.

## *Adirondack Rock*

The Adirondack Mountains are among the oldest in the world and have reached the end of their life cycle, according to geologists. They have become stabilized after aeons of change. We are told that their history is difficult to study out because they are so ancient, but that they were formed because of original internal and upward pressure. Their structure is of two of the oldest types of rock, igneous and metamorphic, with a younger sort, a conglomerate or sedimentary series of strata, formed by the sand and gravel eroded from the older rock.

To the layman, this means that the Adirondacks are composed largely of granite, gneiss and, around the "core," layers of limestone, marble and sandstones, with mica schists and quartzite here and there. No limestone exists in the true "core" of the mountains, hence no true caves, save where limestone intrudes in the lowlands, such as at Lost Pond near Chilson. The caves are therefore "accidental" and "dead," in the high places and amid the great gorges between mountains.

An intrusive rock is the feldspar in several varieties such as anorthosite which appears in labradorite jewelry. This feldspar is the answer to tall tales of "gems and jewels" to be found in the caves and rifts, some of them true, but many exaggerated.

The last stand of Adirondack limestone is the Grenville at the Chimney Rock, an upthrust of this stone which seems almost to have been preserved deliberately by nature as a monument to what once was a mass here. The whole great mass of the Adirondacks, of course, has been glaciated into its present form.

## Garnet Deposits

The sport and science of speleology is closely allied to mineralogy and amateur collecting of minerals, which furnishes a fascinating hobby for many seeking the "jewels of rock" which in late years have been made to reveal startling hues by the use of fluorescent light. Science places garnets under the heading of gems, but at the same time tells us that the highly fractured character of those in New York State deposits renders them unfit for use as jewelry. The principal use of garnets has been as an abrasive, but even that use is being abandoned for synthetic substitutes, just as emery is being replaced by carborundum.

However, the rock splitters seek eagerly for garnets and have a considerable field in the Adirondacks, where some eleven deposits are to be found in the vicinity of the Thirteenth Lake.

Among the finest deposits of the largest garnets are those at the Barton or Moore Mine near North River, described by Geologist Medora Hooper Krieger, whose father, F. C. Hooper, operates one of the group. Garnets have been mined at the Barton deposit since 1882, the earliest of any operation for abrasive uses, and this huge Hooper vein on Gore Mountain gives up the ruby-colored rock to the diameter of ten inches.

Your mineral collector will risk his life and limb to gather even small rock "jewels" of this type—of which there are scores of varying hues and tints to be found. Armed with hammer and chisel, groups of these collectors swarm into dangerous old quarries and pits like small boys seeking buried treasure in a Tom Sawyer cave. I have seen them, in a cold rain, climb onto a steep, crumbling ledge of soft rock to bang loose slabs of it and carry home pounds of it, for a few tiny specks of some tongue-twisting mineral or another, to be viewed with any satisfaction only under a microscope.

## Cave Pearls

Sometimes one finds rockflow or dripstone formations, any of which can be simply classified under the name of travertine, as a general term, in potholes of one sort or another in a cave. Someone has called them, romantically and not inaccurately, cave pearls. They are rounded, like pearls, and some are translucent, some look a bit more like moonstones than pearls, and some are dull and remarkable only for their roundness. They are rare, particularly in caves that have been much visited, because they are so easy to scoop up and carry away, but in at least one cave in New York they are well anchored because of having fallen into or being covered with the natural cement of dissolved and hardened limestone.

You can be fooled, too, for sometimes these formations are merely ordinary pebbles that have been rounded by the friction of flowing water pushing them around and around in a closed receptable of rock.

In Howe Caverns such pebbles have been carefully observed and found to have been cemented into the surface of flowstone since 1928, and firmly imbedded in it. You cannot carry them away.

## *Ice Caves and Gorges*

Besides the several icy gorges and jumbled rock caves to be found in the northern Adirondacks, others are existent in the Catskills and elsewhere.

Stony Clove in the town of Hunter, Green County, northwest of Woodstock, is one. Deep Hollow in Lexington, between the head-waters of the West Kill of Schoharie Creek and the Bush Kill of Esopus Creek is another. These have ice in them until late summer. In a transverse valley crossing westward from the Fishkill and Cold Spring Valley, in Phillipstown, Putnam County, is a deep gorge in the mountains called Hell Hollow, in which ice frequently lies until August and sometimes through the year.

In Petersburg, Rensselaer County, on the slope of Petersburg Mountain, is the Snow Hole, a rift in rock that holds snow until mid-summer, and is often visited by students from Williams College, Williamstown, Massachusetts, for the novelty of having snowball battles in summer. There is said to be a real cave nearby.[2]

## *Rock Houses*

Natural formations resembling Indian shelter caves are found near Colchester in the Catskills where numerous overhanging cliffs occur, caused by the disintegration of particular beds of grey grits

[2]This reputed real cave is probably McMaster's Cave on the Massachusetts side of the mountain, a long, wet, muddy crawl, reported in *New England's Buried Treasure*.

leaving other parts of the same rock, less susceptible of disintegration, to form overhang, arched grottoes, and small caverns.

### *Crooke's Cave*

Dr. Flower reports a cave on the Cohoes quadrangle, southeast of Raymertown on the front of the Rensselaer grit plateau (in Rensselaer County). This cave, at the present time, is little more than a shelter among some loose blocks of a coarse conglomerate which is the basal part of the Rensselaer grit. However, it is interesting because it has been the center of various tales. Many persons assert that the cave was once more extensive, and there are reports, doubtless fantastic, of people entering this cave and coming out on the other side of the hill. One tale is to the effect that "a dog went through, clear under the mountain in the cave and came out on the other side"—wagging his tail, it is to be supposed.

There is a fine cold spring issuing from a rock nearby. The place was formerly popular as a picnic area. It is to be reached by taking a country road east from Raymertown, to the old Downey farm, where another road leads off and a trail proceeds from its ending.

This is known as Cold Spring or Crooke's Cave.

### *Old Maids' Hole*

In the limestone belt of the Fort Ann quadrangle, there is a small cavern northeast of Comstock known to the local inhabitants. It is scarcely more than a rock shelter, but is a true cavern formed by solution in dolomites. Another, and larger cave is to be found on the next hill to the south of this one, but has not been adequately explored.

There is a "beautiful example of a sinkhole" on the western outskirts of Sharon Springs, essentially a chimney, such as leads to many of the caverns of the Alps, and receiving a small trickle of water. A rope is needed to explore this.

(Dr. Flower)

The cave is evidently the Old Maids' Hole, according to Donald L. Palmer of Sidney, an energetic young spelunker, who was "all but drowned trying to get in," he reports, although it is "supposedly a good cave . . . opens at a sinkhole but 50 yards from the highway (U. S. 20) and is shown on the Canajoharie quadrangle map at approximately 74° x 42° 47′. The stream comes from the very small pond, flows underground about ½ mile and comes out in the village (from someone's cellar). The chambers are reputed to be the size of those in Ball's Cave. We intend to go back there during this summer after a dry spell, as drainage from the ice pond makes a descent all but impossible." (March 24, 1947).[3]

## *"The East Caves of Syracuse"*

Out of the clear sky of Utah, in June, 1947 came a strange inquiry about reputed caverns near Syracuse, N. Y. Miss Opal Kemp of 220 Canyon Road, Salt Lake City, made the inquiry, first to the Syracuse Chamber of Commerce, then to the Secretary of State at Albany, and finally to me, through the circulation of one of her letters to officials of the State Museum and the State Department of Conservation, who had an idea that the spelunker from Pittsfield, Massachusetts, would know about them if anyone did.

Miss Kemp had written that "a group of us are planning to visit the east this summer and wish to explore caverns known as 'the East Caves of Syracuse.' These caves are said to be the western entrance to the subterranean passage which extended under the Atlantic Ocean to the British Isles. Parts of the cavern system have collapsed —one as recently as 1928—so that it is now impossible to travel in them. However, the entrances remain intact."

It took but a few minutes of research in the geology department of the State Museum to discover that there actually are some caves east of Syracuse, and that they are curious ones, indeed, and deep and some of them quite long, for in *The Geology of the Syracuse Quadrangle* by Thomas Cramer Hopkins, published as *New York State Museum Bulletin 171,* in 1914, there was found not only an elaborate study of the "East Caves of Syracuse," but photographs taken, exteriorly, of some of the odd crevices, with people perched in them.

These crevices are in Onandaga limestone, which is the hardest kind found in New York State and which spreads clear across the

[3]A return visit on October 12, 1947, resulted in Mr. Palmer and others getting down a shaft about 40 feet—no farther.

Syracuse quadrangle, in some areas forming large, level floors of rock swept free of residual matter by glaciers and the wash of water, and with deep clefts in the rock.

One of these areas lies along the top of a cliff that borders what is known as the Clark Reservation, a state park, about three miles southeast of Syracuse.

As Professor Hopkins describes them,

> At the Syracuse caves, three miles southeast of the city, some of these fissure caverns have been explored to a depth of more than a hundred feet and some hundreds of feet in length. Where this fissuring has been intensified it produces the well-known *karsten* topography.
>
> In a few places there has been a little deposition of calcite on the walls of the fissures, but in general the deposition is very slight in comparison with the solution since most of the material dissolved has been carried away into the streams or deposited in the deeper portions of the underlying rocks.
>
> Some of these fissures are open enough at the top to permit large quantities of snow to enter them during the winter months, and remain in the form of snow and ice during the greater part of the summer, forming what is known locally as the "ice caves." These occur in the cliffs around Blue Lake and at the Split Rock quarries.

This officially confirms Miss Kemp's long-distance tip on caves which, until June, 1947, had completely escaped the attention of present-day geologists, speleologists, and spelunkers as well as the usually alert boosters of the Syracuse Chamber of Commerce, which brings us to the inland and western entrance to that prodigious reputed trans-ocean subway from the United States to the British Isles! But where, oh where is the other end?

Curiously, as this inquiry was being made and investigation made of what would be the longest cavern in the world, there came news from across the waters of the Atlantic of the exploration of what is said to be the deepest cavern in the world!

This is in a mountain near Grenoble, France, known as *Dent de Crolles,* which, according to a copyrighted article in the *New York Herald-Tribune* by John O'Reilly, a staff correspondent, is 2,265 feet deep, and its exploration to that depth by French speleologists takes from Italy the long-held record for the deepest cavern, the Great Hole of Preta, near Verona, which is 2,193 feet deep.

"America has some large caverns, but falls far short of the record for depth," wrote Mr. O'Reilly, who made the arduous mountain climb and cave descent in person, with Pierre Chevalier, president of the *Speleo-Club Alpin de Lyon,* and fellow members of the club in May, 1947.

But America may find that it holds the record for the longest cave in the world beneath its land, if these East Caves of Syracuse do now or ever did extend from cliffs of the Syracuse area across under the ocean to the British Isles, for it is some two hundred miles from Syracuse to the Atlantic Coast.

It develops that the Geology Department of Syracuse University made some study of the caves, and that parties of students, with an instructor, used to explore the deep clefts, using ropes, and actually have gone down as deep as 100 feet in them. Among those who have explored the caves is Professor Louis W. Ploger of the Geology Department, who was a student during the time such field trips were being made.

We are indebted to Dr. John G. Broughton, acting state geologist at Albany, for the first official information on these caves, and at the same time for a report on other curious and huge cave formations.

## *Church Cave*

Besides the Stone Church Cavern at Dover Plains, there is a Church Cave in Albany County, very recently explored by Edwin B. Judd, of Schenectady. It rambles about amid the maze of underground drainage passages in the vicinity of Thompson's Lake. It was named for a church nearby, bearing no resemblance to such an edifice itself.

Mr. Judd located it as a result of building a summer camp on the south shore of the lake. He found that the subterranean outlet of the lake was right beneath his cottage and that the hidden stream emerged one and one-half miles southwest in one of four brooks that join. The entrance is opposite the Raymond J. Betts home on a road leading to the General Electric television station. This road cuts across from the Thacher Park Road, east and west. The portal to the cave is so hidden and difficult to find that some help from a member of the Betts family is needed, even for those who have visited it.

It is a very watery cavern until late summer. Mr. Judd has mapped it, and shows it to be a rambling, narrow maze of passages running in all directions for several hundred feet. It is studded with fossils on the walls, sharp projections in the Onondaga limestone, which has been worn away by water so that the fossils stick out and tear clothing to shreds. They have been identified as mostly *zaphrenitis prolifica* and *branchiopods spirifer duodenaris.*

In mid-May Church Cave was filled completely with water, and it is negotiable with any safety or comfort only after mid-August.

This area contains several small, connecting caves and two large ones—Church Cave and another as yet unnamed. Formations in Church Cave suggest such names as The Guillotine, The Cleaver, and The Keyhole.

Mr. Judd, an enthusiastic member of the N.S.S., also names a Devil's Hole, which he says is also known as Skull Cave, previously mentioned in the main text of this book. An acquaintance of his has explored it and describes it as "quite long and narrow and located about five-eighths of a mile northwest of Knox Cave," whose owner, D. C. Robinson, has been vainly attempting to get permission to explore its legendary mysteries.

The Thompson Lake area is described by geologists as a large sinkhole, with the lake occupying the northern end of the sink, and with no surface outlet. Its waters flow underground in Church Cave for about a mile and a half, to appear on the Pitcher farm to the southwest.

The Church Cave was discovered by Professor John H. Cook in 1915, but he published no report on it. In 1930 it was rediscovered by Professor Cleland, of Williams College, and an official report made to the State Museum on its extent and geological features. He describes the phenomenon as follows:

> Except in the spring or after a season of heavy rains the evaporation from the surface of the lake about equals the inflow. The outlet of the lake is in a small cave at the southern end through wide solution joint fissures. When the lake level is high the water pours through this cave in large volume, coming to the surface again in a deep spring on the Pitcher farm, one and a half miles to the southwest. The water flows out here in about the same volume that it is seen to pour through the cave from the lake. It has been stated that sawdust placed in the lake has come out in the pool and that a pickerel from the lake once was found floating in the spring, but there seems to be some doubt about this. (From *Geology of the Berne Quadrangle,* by Winifred Goldring, Assistant State Paleontologist, New York State Museum.)

# *APPENDIX*

## *Cramer's Caves*

Church Cave is described by Seward Cramer as having an entrance in a "honeycombed sort of effect," the joint crack evidently enlarged by solution, and it is believed that the lake is emptied through this cave and emerges as a spring on a farm about two miles away.

Cramer also noted in this vicinity what he called Daddy Longlegs Cave, though it had another name—a very narrow crawl-opening but with some crystals, and the roof swarming with moths, spiders, daddy longlegs, and bats. The bats need not go out hunting insect food.

He also lists Forgotten Cave in the same area, and says that its mouth is so closely overhung with rock it is difficult to get out of it. Some flowstone formations like curtains were found on the walls.

Joober's Hole is one to hunt for. It is said by Cramer to be near Schoharie; he calls it "one of those legendary places that is supposed to be enormous and deep but no one has ever found it."

Seward B. Cramer, early in 1941, began the ambitious project of collecting material for and writing a book on the caverns of America. Within little more than a year he had traveled thousands of miles and visited scores of caves and had gathered a vast amount of material about caves, enough to make a file weighing over eighty pounds. In the spring of 1942 he enlisted in the Army Air Forces and fought in the Pacific Islands. In November, 1944, he was killed in the explosion of his plane as he was returning to this country.

He held the rank of Lieutenant Colonel at the time of his death, having risen from the rank of Captain. Before he went into uniform he had drafted an outline for his proposed book, had taken many pictures of caves, largely in the south, southwest, and northwest, and had arranged for publication of the book. Through the kindness of his widow, Mrs. Louise L. Cramer, of New York City, all this material was turned over to me to assist in the writing and publication of "The American Cave Series."

This is by way of special acknowledgement and in memory of the intrepid caveman that he was. He had tackled a project which has not been done in any comprehensive degree in the history of this country and seemed fairly well on the way to accomplishing it.

Seward Cramer was a native of Ann Arbor, Michigan, and a graduate of the University of Michigan in 1923. He the spent three years in China for an oil company. He was always interested in exploration and was an active member of the Explorers' Club. For several years, just prior to going into the Army, he was editor of the *Explorers' Club Journal,* in which he published several articles on caves. He led groups of the club on cave expeditions. He was also in contact with the infant National Speleological Society and with many speleologists and spelunkers around the country. It is with the deepest appreciation and gratitude that I am able to make use of this valuable material, only a few little items of which appear here, for his work in the East had been awaiting him until after the war.

### *Becker's Cave*

A recent exploration of this long-known cave in Schoharie County was made by Mineralogist Anthony W. Thurston, of Swansea, Massachusetts, and reported in *Rocks and Minerals* magazine, December, 1942. He found it rather difficult to explore—a "fat man's misery"—with loose stones to crawl over and considerable water, including a small lake about 130 feet in.

Mr. Thurston also explored Ball's Cave and Hailes' Cavern and one just east of the village of Gallupville, which he calls Gallupville Cave, that has running water in it, two tufa dams, and one "unusually fine stalactite . . . but the water is too deep to get up close to it conveniently." Rubber boots are recommended to wade in as the water is mostly 2 feet deep.

### *Hudson Valley Caves*

Peter Zodac, editor of *Rocks and Minerals,* seems to have discovered a Money Hole Cave with an interesting tradition. Located about ¾ of a mile east of Nelson Corners on the Albany Post Road, 8 miles north of Peekskill, it is, he says, a cave in granite, pegmatite, and gneiss about 30 by 30 feet in area from 4 to 7 feet high, and entered by a 3-foot opening, with a drop of 15 feet just inside.

According to Dr. G. P. Wygant, a historian of Peekskill, "the cave was a counterfeiter's den, used by one, Henry Holmes, around 1820. A farmer while hunting for his cattle discovered the cave and reported the presence of a counterfeiter and Holmes was arrested and sent to prison for seven years. Mr. Zodac, who visited it in November,

1938, found nothing of interest in it. The counterfeit money hadn't drawn any interest.

Mr. Zodac also visited a noted cave in jumbled rocks in the Blue Mountain Reservation, on the northern slope of Spitzenberg Mountain, 2 miles south of Peekskill, which he measured at 15 by 12 by 5 feet, with no formations, and he reported no tall tale about it.

Most intriguing is an under-water cave said to exist at Verplanck's Point, with an opening on the edge of the east shore of the Hudson River, but although Mr. Zodac was guided to where it was said to be by an old gentleman who had "heard where it was when he was a boy, no trace of it could be found."

Tradition has it that it is a vast cavern that "comes out somewhere but where is uncertain; also that it was known to the Indians, was used as a hideout by smugglers and that the bones of horses have been seen on the floor." Mr. Zodac warns that the whole story may be a myth, or anyway, that the cave is just a hollowed-out hole in rock, formed by the tides. No hole was too small for this rock hunter, for he investigated one in the Depew Woods, about a mile south of Peekskill, only 8 by 2 by 6 feet in size, out of whose crevices trees were growing. He proposed to visit it in 1949 to see how much more the trees had grown and what they do to the joints in the rock.

## *Continentalville Cave*

"This is the rarest of caves in the Hudson Valley," says Mr. Zodac, "and the only one known to the writer. This is in the historic little hamlet of Continentalville, about three miles north of Peekskill, and was formed by a split in the pegmatite in a hillside, which formed a room, beyond a narrow opening, some fifty-five feet long and seven feet high, three feet wide," with faint traditions as a Tory hideout.

## *Ithaca Caves*

An expert spelunker, Alfred W. Nyquist, while attending Cornell University, located three caves about 3½ miles north, and a fourth about 13 miles southeast, of Ithaca, and found them a challenge to the rugged rock climber as well. The trio of caves to the north is near the Portland Point cement factory and is to be approached by following the railroad that bears cement to Ithaca, a distance of about 1/4 mile, to a cliff wherein appears a rectangular hole about 6 feet high and 4 feet wide.

A second cave, 500 feet on, hides itself behind a rock and discharges a small stream in time of thaw. A third, 300 feet farther on, is at the head of a stream bed. All three caves are about five-sixths of the way up a 45-degree hill.

Nyquist, an N.S.S. member, went barefooted in February into the second cave, and found it only 10 feet deep, and the water very cold, indeed, so that his exploring was done in a hurry. He found a fissure in the ceiling, 2 inches by 18 inches, at an angle of 60 degrees with the forward horizon, and no progress possible beyond the 10 feet —even with bare feet.

The third cave seemed to be quite extensive, as bats flew out of it and back in, vanishing behind the face of the rock. A rope would be needed to get into it, as the entrance is made difficult by overhang, requiring approach along a narrow ledge of shale. A small "rain shelter" was found about 40 feet south of this cave, with an opening at both ends.

Three miles south of Slaterville on a knoll is a cave of sorts, as reported by local inhabitants, but no description of it could be obtained.

## *Fossil Caves at Forge Hollow*

A scarab fossil now in the Metropolitan Museum of New York City is one of the finds made in one of two caves at Forge Hollow, which lies between Waterville and Deansboro, in Madison County. The fossil was found by Amos Osborne, of Waterville, and others have picked up such relics there. The caves, adjacent to each other, have no local name but might well be called Phinney's Forge Caves, for a man by that name had a forge near them. There used to be a dam opposite the caves which formed a pond that spread over a considerable area, and water from it furnished power to operate the forge. It has long been gone and the pond bed drained.

The caves are interesting in winter for the ice cascades that form over their entrances and which jam up the insides. A legend has it that an early explorer found a good-sized lake in one of the caves, long ago, and that ghostly events took place in them. They are "crawl caves," low and tortuous.

Lt. Col. (then Capt.) Seward S. Cramer, A.A.F.

Before Burrough's Cave, Slide Mountain, in the Catskills, Miss Bess Little, of Menands, marks her 48th peak over 4,000 feet high

# APPENDIX

## A Cave Reservoir

The City of Hudson was at one time supplied with water from a limestone spring on the northwest base of Becraft Mountain, and another spring, emerging from the eastern base, gave forth warm water, when examined by geologists. It tasted like brook water. It was supposed to be the outlet of a small brook that sank into the fissures of the limestone in a sinkhole on the top of the mountain.

## Pothole Caves

Potholes of a size to be considered open caves have been found in strangely elevated situations in several places in York State. There is one at Little Falls and another in Antwerp, St. Lawrence County. The latter was described by Professor E. Emmons, one of Mather's collaborators in the compiling, in 1842, of the mammoth volume titled *Natural History of New York State*:

> It is at least one hundred feet above the Oswegatchie, three-quarters of a mile distant, with an intervening hill higher by some fifty feet than this remarkable hole. This hole is from twenty-four to thirty feet deep and twelve to fourteen feet in diameter, bearing the usual marks, on the interior of water worn surfaces.

This and other potholes were believed to have been formed during the "glacial drift" which planed away some higher elevations, leaving these exposed after the ice had gone.

Excavations at Little Falls that were being made during the spring of 1947 to carve a new channel for the Mohawk River and eliminate a "death curve" on the New York Central Railroad in that narrow gorge and five-ply parallel routes of transportation, revealed what Dr. Broughton agrees (with Historian Nelson Greene, of Little Falls) are "the largest and most remarkable on earth."

Blasting revealed one that measures 82 feet by 56 feet, rivaling one 80 by 60 feet which was blown open when the Barge Canal was being built; and some that were being revealed as this is written were described as having "no bottom yet found."

These holes are in syenite rock, of extreme and uniform hardness, and it lies in the narrowest pass in eastern United States where man has had to fight his way through for river transport, canal transport, railroads, trolley roads, and highways.

## *A Chimney Cave*

In the limestone belt of the Fort Ann quadrangle, northeast of Comstock, is a small cave known to the local inhabitants. It is scarcely more than a rock shelter, but is a true cavern formed by solution in dolomites. Another and larger cave is to be found on the next hill to the south of this one, but it has not been adequately explored.

There is a "beautiful example of a sinkhole" on the western outskirts of Sharon Springs, essentially a chimney, such as leads to many of the caverns of the Alps, which receives a small trickle of water. A rope is needed to explore this.

## *Perry's Cave*

We give you also Perry's Cave, at Frankfort, on the Mohawk, Herkimer County. It has been a long chase but we have run it to earth. This cave, according to David H. Beetle in his book, *West Canada Creek,* was named for Oliver Curtis Perry, "the famous train robber." No relation so far as we can discover, despite the coincidence of "Oliver" and "Perry," and the fact that at Put-in-Bay, Ohio, there is another Perry's Cave, named for Commodore Oliver Hazard Perry, from whom we can claim collateral descent.

This train-robber Perry, Mr. Bettle says, may have been the fugitive who one night appeared at a brick house in Fairfield, the only brick house in the village, opposite Trinity Episcopal Church, "hid in a clothes press and—impeccably dressed—came downstairs later, apologized rather inadequately that he'd 'felt sleepy and gone up to lie down,' and disappeared into the night," after the sheriff's posse had passed on.

That is all that seems to be known about Perry's Cave.

## Notes from *The Story of Crown Point Iron*

by Dr. E. Eugene Barker, of Albany

(Continued from Chapter 17)

**(This hitherto unpublished account of the once mighty mines of Crown Point, Mineville, and vicinity, comes from a most exhaustive study made by Dr. Barker for the New York Historical Society. The facts here set down are taken from his manuscript, which was intended originally as an appendix to the story which was published in *New York History* magazine.)**

# *APPENDIX*

The first discovery of iron ore in Crown Point was made in 1818 at what was later known as the Saxe or Saxe & Floyd bed. Two years later it was opened, and in 1823 this ore was used in a forge established at a water power site on a stream nearby. Quantities of it were taken to a furnace owned and operated by Jacob Saxe, near the mouth of the Salmon River, Clinton County, and there worked.

Described by Emmons in his report on the geology of New York (1842) as a peroxide, having the form and structure of the magnetic oxide, reddish brown in color. Usually referred to as hematite . . . Emmons said (1848), "this mine has been abandoned for many years."

The old workings may still be found about one mile or so above Crown Point Center near where Gold Brook runs into Putnam Creek on the road between Ironville and White Church. They are surprisingly large as judged by the standards of their time. The forge of John Renne was at upper falls of Putnam Creek, a short distance above Crown Point Center on what is locally called the "Creek Road."

Emmons states there were two or three other localities in town where a red ore was obtained, but not in sufficient quantities to be worth working for forge and furnace. They were used for paints, to a limited extent. Other deposits were so heavily impregnated with sulfur as to be unsuitable at the time. Two deep shafts in the north face of Breed Hill, south of Crown Point village, and a third one over 80 feet deep in the eastern face of the hill known as the Gunnison Mine are still to be seen; they were worked by the Hammonds shortly after the Civil War, so far as can be ascertained.

Irondale, later Ironville, is about 6 miles west of Lake Champlain. Putnam Creek was dammed there to form a pond over a mile and a half long, furnishing motive power for the plant (Penfield Bed).

A visitor to this locality in 1874 describes what he saw:

> Everything hereabouts wearing the black, sooty look which is so common to all iron manufacturing places. This is a small village, lying at the north side of the track, and you are at once struck with the air of neatness which the little white cottages lining the street bear. Here is a nice church, a school-house, a neatly kept cemetery on the hill, a six-bloomer forge, first erected in 1828 by Penfield, Harwood & Co., sawmill, gristmill, separator, etc. A new separator and roasting kilns are being built beneath a new stone dam which from all appearances will furnish whatever water-power is needed, Put's Creek here making up in

head what it lacks in volume. All about are evidences of the devastation which follows the bloomer iron works—the hills are stripped of their timber far up towards their summits, and way up by the margin of the forest you see the old-fashioned coal pits smoking. . . .

The same visitor describes the village of Hammondville, where the mines are located and its scenery:

We gaze about on one of the roughest and rockiest of scenes. Huge, bare rocks rise to the left, while in front, belonging to the same range (the Kayderosseras) is Knob Mountain, a bare, round rock, having a perpendicular precipice upon the western side, from five to eight hundred feet high. . . . Mount Marcy towers up to the northwest but his companions are hidden by the nearer ranges. Owl's Pate is a most remarkably shaped mountain in the same direction and a little to the right of Mount Marcy, a huge, smooth, round-topped rock with a precipitous bluff to the south, this and its near neighbors shutting off the view of Nipple Top and Dix's Peak. But down in the valley of the Schroon, the view is very fine, with the gentle slopes on either side, while the bald wall of Knob Mountain to the east shows to best advantage, the rays of the sun striking it at right angles and bringing out all the rich variety of colors which the oxides of iron impart to the rocks in this region. At the foot of this bluff lies Hammond Lake, of fabulous depth, into which were put 25,000 young salmon trout over a year ago, and from which rare sport and rarer eating are anticipated in the future. (Knob Pond—this body of water has never been known by any other name—the salmon trout, if ever planted in it, did not thrive, as these anticipated results were never realized. E.E.B.)

The foreign workmen here are mostly Swedes, with a few Danes and Norwegians, and are intelligent, frugal and industrious. We see here the same style of neat, white cottages (Brandon Brown paint was the only color used. W.C.N.) which were noted at Irondale. The company owns them all and the workmen have the use of them, rent free, as also they do the pasturage for their cows during these dull times. No liquor is allowed about the premises, and no swearing is heard or abuse of horses permitted. The foundations of a church are already laid. The foreign workmen at present are mostly Lutherans, but all demoninations will have a chance in the new church, and all preparations are being made for a large population. At present only about a hundred men are being employed but there is ample room in the separate mines for ten times that number when they are all worked, but now just enough to keep the blast furnaces running at Crown Point, with a sufficient quantity ahead to keep it supplied for 6 months. These buildings have all been erected within the past twelve months, since the railroad was commenced in the spring of 1873.

The use of the electric magnet at the Irondale foundry contributed in an indirect way to the evolution of one of the most important inventions that has ever revolutionized the world's industries—the electric motor, invented by a Vermont blacksmith, Thomas Davenport, of Brandon, who went to Crown Point to see the magnetic device that would lift an anvil. He wanted if possible to buy it, found no one at home, and went to see Professor Joseph Henry in Albany, who was also away, then returned to Crown Point, with his brother, Oliver, an itinerant clock tinker and tin peddler. They saw the electric magnet, a bar of iron shaped like a horseshoe, the arms wound with wire, each about ten inches long, with a spread of six inches. They bought it for seventy-five dollars, raising the money by selling all Oliver's stock in trade, swapping his horse for a poorer one, and pooling all cash to get the coveted treasure.

On his return to Brandon, Davenport spent most of the night taking it apart to learn what made it work, while his wife took notes. He made a new one, much larger and more powerful, his wife furnishing silk for the winding by tearing up her wedding dress.

Davenport thought of the magnet not as a mere curiosity or wonder but "a mighty force of nature capable of doing a great work." He would turn wheels with this force; and against heartbreaking struggles with adverse circumstances, he invented an electric motor, the precursor of all electric machinery and transportation of the modern age.[1]

General John Hammond was president of the Crown Point Company. A veteran of the Civil War, and highly respected, he was a striking figure on the black horse that had carried him safely through the campaigns.

When labor difficulties arose he settled them in a manner more characteristic of those times than of these. In a letter dated January 14, 1941, W. C. Northey tells of "an attempted strike that took place in the fall of 1873, called a 'Swede strike' although none of our good loyal Swedes had anything to do with it. It was promoted by outside parties and attempted by a bunch of floaters who went to a saloon at Paradox on a Saturday morning and got liquored up, decided to strike, picked up clubs and started to the pits, recruiting en route to Hammondville."

General Hammond was advised by wire, got on a locomotive with a constable, and raced from Crown Point to Hammondville in twenty-five minutes, a record for the ore railroad. He took a short

[1]In the light of recent discovery this claim may be somewhat mistaken.

cut from the Penfield Pit to the top of North Pit Hill, arriving in time to see the strikers coming around a bend in the road. He halted them with an old army pistol about a foot long, drove them to the scale house, where he discussed the matter with them at the point of his big pistol, had two of them arrested and jailed, and thereby quelled the strike so effectively that there never were any more at the mines.

Mr. Northey moved from Minneapolis to Hammondville in 1873, and he tells of the crude methods of mining used at the time. Sledge hammers were swung to break up chunks of the hard ore, and one giant of a man, Pat Gorman, was paid double wages because of his strength and skill with sledge and drill. Only three pits were worked then, but finally as many as fifty were opened and 750 men were employed. Miners dug in all directions until the ore got so thin that a man could not work between the "hanging wall" and the "foot wall" of rock. They left pillars of ore for safety, until the veins ran thin and gave out; then removed the pillars, working back and up to the entrance. The Hammond Pit was cleaned out in the late '70's and the Penfield Pit in the late '80's.

Diamond drilling failed to disclose any good deposits deeper down and the place was entirely abandoned. In 1900 Mr. Northey, on opening some new mines for the American Steel and Wire Company at Hibbing, Minnesota, found four carloads of machinery from Hammondville, the last shipment over the Crown Point Railroad made before the rails were taken up.

Nature's reclamation of the site was hastened by reforestation. In the period between 1904 and 1909 some 1,200 to 1,500 acres were planted to pine and Norway spruce by the American Steel and Wire Company, forming dense thickets, and hiding many of the remains.

Dr. Barker lists a dozen sites where workings were located in the Crown Point iron area, including blast furnaces, ore pits, forges, charcoal furnaces, and quarries where limestone was dug out.

## *Old Lead Mines*

More than a century and a quarter ago lead was revealed to white men by Indians who had found it in a marsh at Ellenville, and as a result shafts were bored into a hill, some 600 feet, according to report, but "more lead was found in the marsh than in the mine," according to geologists. Some zinc and some silver were reported found also.

There was a lead mine known as the Shawangunk Lead Mine, two miles northeast of Winstboro, in Sullivan County, that was discovered by a hunter. When first opened, masses of galena were taken out, weighing 800, 1,000, and 1,400 pounds each and shipped to New York City for analysis.

Several graphite mines have been worked throughout the state, one of the oldest and best known near Lake George in the famous Graphite Hill that rises along the main highway east of the lake, a terror to motorists in early days of the automobile because of the steepness of the hill and the slippery coating of graphite that was washed onto the road in rains. This is the old Lakeside Mine, at one time operated by the Dixon Crucible Company, for the filling of lead pencils, which, as every schoolboy knows, is not lead at all. These mines are mostly open quarries, hardly to be considered either as real mines or as caverns, but of interest for their uses.

## *The National Speleological Society*

This is the first and only organization of its kind in America, save for some small groups of spelunkers, such as one that existed in New England in the early 1930's and one in Washington, D. C., at about the same time. The N.S.S. was formed in 1940, with a grotto or chapter in the District of Columbia, and one in New England, with headquarters at Pittsfield, Massachusetts. This one, called the New England Spelunkers' Grotto, No. 1, was organized December 1, 1940, in a cave in Lanesboro, Massachusetts, known as Pettibone Falls Cave. Since then the society has spread its membership throughout the United States, Mexico, France and England, and has over seven hundred members at the present writing.

At its annual meeting at the United States National Museum, Washington, February 22-23, 1947, a campaign was launched to put the society on a permanent financial basis. It had received the warm endorsement of the Government for its work in exploring underground sites, and success seems guaranteed.

Impetus was given to the forming of such a national body by the publication of *Underground New England—Tall Tales of Small Caves,* in 1939,[2] which revealed to the public that while there were

[2]By Clay Perry.

one or perhaps two cave societies in the British Isles, and a whole literature and bibliography about their caves, no such organization existed in America and no organized effort was being made to survey our thousands of caverns.

In a very short time the N.S.S. had become so well organized and operated that it was publishing a monthly news-letter to members and a semi-annual bulletin, collecting a library of all literature to be found, compiling a library of cave photographs and films, and methodically listing all the known caves explored or reported.

Speleology, the science of caves and caverns, and spelunking, the sport of cave exploring, have been closely allied on the field trips and meetings. Scientific aims have attracted to the N.S.S. many notable persons, the heads of museums and university departments, geologists, and paleontologists, and has won it the sponsorship, formal or informal, of such institutions as the Smithsonian Institution, at Washington, the Academy of Natural Sciences, in Philadelphia, and several others, most of them institutional members of the N.S.S.

Spelunking is a new sort of sport to most persons. It has attracted the adventurous to mingle with the scientists and give themselves little aid in their work. The collecting and recording of the history, legend, and folklore of caverns has proved one of the most fascinating parts of the program, and it is for this purpose, largely, that "The American Cave Series" has been planned, with the approval of the National Speleological Society, and with great assistance given the author and publisher by the society as a whole and its members in various localities.

The N.S.S. grew most rapidly in membership during 1946 when two hundred new members were added and several new grottoes formed. The address of the society is Room 510, Star Building, Washington, D. C.

## *"Safer in a Cave Than in a Car"*

A statement to this effect has been made and repeated scores of times with sincere conviction by many a cave explorer. It seems to have originated with Russell Trall Neville, of Kewanee, Illinois, premiere spelunker, who calls himself, with good reason, The Cave Man. Mr. Neville, who since 1920 has been exploring caverns all over this country and Mexico, and is believed to have traveled at least 5,000 miles underground while taking as many or more photographs for his illustrated lectures on caves, ought to know.

His worst injury suffered in a cave was a banged knee which developed interior trouble in the joint and laid him up for some time, but he came near to death while driving his automobile on a slippery winter road in Maine, hastening to keep a lecture engagement.

It is safer in a cave than in a car, even when the car is standing still, according to one of the officials of the N.S.S. He tells this one on his own wife, after swearing his listeners to secrecy, so far as the identity of the lady is concerned:

After this lady had crawled, waded, climbed, wormed and swum through the famous Sinks of Gandy Creek in West Virginia, a mile-long cavern with a river flowing through it, she was changing from wet clothing to her street wear outfit in her car and *sprained her back trying to put on her girdle!*

# A CAVE INDEX AND GUIDE

The following index contains the name of all the known caves in New York State, so far as the author and many helpers have been able to learn in some years of exploration and research. Most of those in the list are described or at least mentioned in the text. If no page numbers appear, no descriptions will be found. In some cases reports of caves have come to the author too late for exploration and inclusion of material.

A few mines, quarries, and other hollows in the earth are listed and described for their unusual human interest. It is hoped that this alphabetical index may be of help to the reader and especially to the active and eager explorer of the Underground Empire.

Altogether some 250 natural caves in New York State are herewith listed, all of them known, and most of them having names. A few recently reported caves in New England not listed in "New England's Buried Treasure," the first volume of "The American Caves Series," are appended, separately. Subjects other than caves are indexed for special interest which they hold.

The last expedition and attempt at exploration made by the author was with a group of students from Rensselaer Polytechnic Institute at Troy who are members of the Rensselaer Outing Club, which is affiliated with the Intercollegiate Outing Clubs Association. It ended in disappointment. A forgotten limestone cave near Hoag's Corners on property owned by A. Douglas Schleif, of Stephentown Center, mentioned on page 26, could be squirmed into only about 40 feet when the spelunkers were stopped by a rockfall and were in danger of being pinned down by other loose rocks in the ceiling. The owner planned to dig and blast in an attempt to open a cavern reputed to be long.

# INDEX

# *INDEX*

# *INDEX*



NEW ENGLAND CAVES
RECENTLY REPORTED

Indian Caves, on Indian Mountain, near Indian Lake, a few yards off N. Y. 4, from Millerton, N. Y. Artifacts have been found here.

Calvin's Cave, Chippenhook, Vermont. A reputed Tory Cave.